THE NATURE OF HUMAN NATURE

THE NATURE OF HUMAN NATURE

Alex Comfort

HARPER & ROW, PUBLISHERS

NEW YORK AND EVANSTON

This book was originally published in England
under the title *Nature and Human Nature*.

FIRST U.S. EDITION

LIBRARY OF CONGRESS CATALOG CARD NUMBER: *67-15973*

Contents

Illustrations

Chapter 1

Human Biology -
The Study of Man

If we met an Englishman or an American who lived two hundred years ago, we should not find him – clothing and habits apart – visibly different from ourselves. We would not find it odd that he should lack some experiences that we find commonplace – he would never have flown, or taken a hot bath with running water. There are Englishmen and Americans today who have done neither. It might be harder, for some of us, at least, to communicate with him if we realized that he would never, for example, have heard a modern orchestra, and that if he were married he would expect, in the natural course of events, to lose one or two of his children from disease. Yet there are still people among us who would be in the same position. He would, however, be fundamentally separated from us in another way – a way which would make him more like his ancestor of two hundred years earlier still, or four hundred, or even six hundred, than to his descendant today. What would cut him off from us would be his attitude to himself, his estimate of Man. It probably did not feel any different to be alive two hundred or six hundred or even six thousand years ago, from the standpoint of ordinary bodily sensations – the sources of comfort and discomfort were the same; what has changed, and more rapidly in the last two hundred than in the preceding six thousand years, is the built-in picture of Man in Man's own mind. Being human does not feel different, but 'thinks' different.

Primitive Man – if that is the word for skilful, social and intelligent peoples like the Bushmen and the Aborigines – are not really very remote from us in most of their concerns; the superficial differences are in custom, and are not more fundamental than the less striking differences in custom which separate Englishmen from Americans. Where they do differ markedly from us is in their deep concern with rituals and activities which, though purposive, are not purposive in the way that hunting, toolmaking, or even praying are purposive – dances, ceremonies, stories and the like which serve to keep intact a sense of relation with their fellows in the tribe, with their ancestors, and, in an unexpressed way, with the rest of creation. If they verbalize these concerns they do so by talking about a 'dream time', which is myth, not history, rather than by explicit statements about Man. This crop of concerns and myths is important, because though for modern men it is no longer an important social activity, second only to eating and mating, it is still stored in the attic. We and our eighteenth-century ancestor both shared it with the Bushman, though it has taken the development of psychoanalysis to bring it out into daylight.

Later or more sophisticated Man, who built towns and practised agriculture instead of hunting and food-gathering, expressed the same concerns in explicit statements – either by treating the older myths as history, or by using their heads, as the Greek or Indian philosophers did, to try to formulate ideas about the place of Man in the generality of things. Some cultures, like the ancient Mediterranean civilizations which gave us the Bible, saw Man as a special creation, halfway between a deity and an animal, but definitely superior in status and prestige to other creatures. Others, like the ancient Hindus, saw all living and non-living objects, Man included, as a combined expression of Something (Mind, God, or Intelligence – a point of view known as pantheism) and consequently stressed the community of Man with animals – in one of which one might become reincarnated. With the still further growth of techniques and of systematized patterns of ideology, Man got surer and surer about himself, expressing his self-estimate in religious and philosophical terms, but always tending more and more to give himself a special and a unique status over brute beasts, Nature and even 'savages' who lacked this clear appreciation of the duties and privileges of humanness. Two hundred years ago, our ancestor, intelligent or not, would have stood in this tradition – not so fully in it as his medieval ancestor, who lived in a cosy world which was the physical centre of creation, with God above it and only devils below, but still, in that world. He would have stood in the same tradition whether he was a Christian, a Deist, or a philosophic atheist – it was in the intellectual air which everyone breathed. But in the years between him and us, something radical happened to that self-estimate.

What has, in fact, happened is that the relationship between Man and 'Nature', i.e. things outside himself, which the Aborigine expressed intuitively and the pre-technical Man theorized about, can now be put into words in a testable form. It has been brought, like so much else, within the scope of the method of intelligent guess followed by verification which has yielded such tremendous intellectual dividends in every field where it has been applied – the scientific method. Before this could happen, the culture which was to undertake that application had to go through the disturbing intellectual and emotional experience of making the break with former self-estimates, most of them as old as civilization, and some probably as old as Man. The shock did not lie in realizing that human beings have elements in common with the 'lower' animals – that had long been recognized. It lay in the recognition that cherished human behaviour and attitudes, as well as such processes as thinking, loving, producing art and all the other activities which we traditionally accept as 'ours', were now within the scope of the same sceptical method which could be used to elucidate the ways of animals: that Man was subject to study and experiment, not at a different rate of exchange, but at the same rate of exchange as the rest of Nature. Just how disturbing a prospect

3

that was can be seen from the anxiety which some people would feel even now in reading such a formulation – a fear, chiefly, that ideas of value would be left out of account. They need not be; in fact, the growth of a level and steady self-awareness has strengthened the basis for them, and for the sense of human uniqueness. But it took time to get over the shock.

The occasion of the change was Darwin's demonstration that men were directly descended from animals. This was neither a new idea (others had repeatedly suggested that it would prove to be so) nor the outcome of a sudden discovery – all Darwin did was to organize facts which were already known to most naturalists and scientists of his time. His own major contribution was in pointing out how the development had probably come about. Yet with intellectual, as with political revolutions, gradual processes have a way of coming to a head when a large backlog of new thinking, long overdue, has to be done in a short time. The *Origin of Species* triggered a revolution of this kind. It was not only that Darwin's view of Man contradicted older ideas of Biblical infallibility – not all Darwin's contemporaries viewed the Book of Genesis as history, or were greatly upset at the suggestion that it was not. The new thing which had to be fitted into the intellectual landscape, not only of biologists or theologians, but of everyone, was the evolutionary picture of Man. To us now, perhaps, this does not look like a big change. Linnaeus, who classified animals and plants, had classified Man along with the animals, as the highest of them, calling him *Homo sapiens*, Man the Knowing. Physicians had long experimented on animals in the hope and belief (often over-sanguine) that the results would hold for human patients. We were obviously mammals – we suckled our young. Yet it was not until Darwin's day that the growth of society, of attitudes to religion and progress, and of biology itself all reached the point at which the emotional as well as the purely intellectual realization of our historical continuity with the rest of nature could 'click', and the result was a profound and irreversible change in our awareness.

4

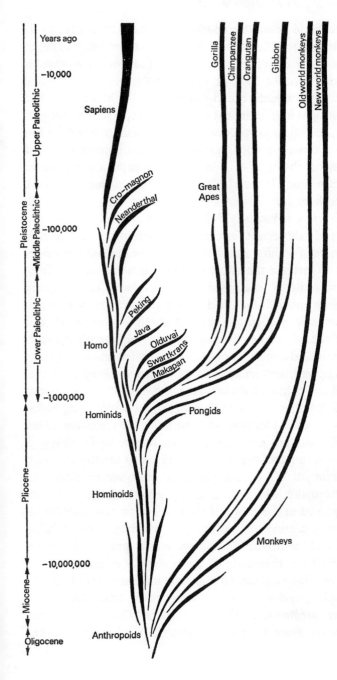

FIG. 1.—Lines of descent that lead to Man and his closer relatives are charted. The hominoid superfamily diverged from the anthropoid line in the Miocene period some twenty million years ago. From the hominoid line came the tool-using hominids at the beginning of the Pleistocene. The genus *Homo* appeared in the hominid line during the first interglacial; the species *Homo sapiens*, around 50,000 years ago.

There was to be another equally severe though more gradually accepted change within the century, when anthropologists began to shake the self-confidence of civilized European Man that his civilization was the only, or the naturally correct, sort – and when finally Sigmund Freud demonstrated to him that he had no real insight into his motives, and that in spite of the Enlightenment, and of the post-Darwinian rationalism of which he was already becoming proud, he shared and was influenced by the forces of which the Aborigine was aware in his description of the 'dream time'. It was the last brick of the evolutionary wall. Eighteenth-century Man was on the other side of that wall. His universe was basically different from ours.

The main difference, intellectually speaking, is that ours is much more of a unity than his. Now we see the same processes at work to increase the elaboration of plants and animals from simple to complex forms, then to the evolution of a thinking and feeling animal which had conceptual thought, was social, developed a body of custom and of transmitted knowledge, and finally fathered us, the observer or reader today, with the body of a mammal, the unconscious and social needs and drives of an Aborigine, and the accumulated experience of living matter in our cells and of human tradition in our heads and books: we can fit in the inanimate universe as well, and the whole thing makes continuous sense. Oddly enough, with this full realization, Man still looks unique, and this does not appear to be simply a reflection of the fact that men are composing the theory which makes him so. We do not yet know the basic time-cycle of galaxy formation which is our first point of reference for what has happened in the past – there is still argument whether all matter was created at one time, or whether it keeps being formed and destroyed in an open-ended process. In either event, the basic time-scale of the behaviour of matter at this level is very long indeed, and its basic mechanism is physical – the simple physico-chemical interaction of units, ranging in size from subatomic particles to galaxies. This is, as it were, evolutionary Stage I. Stage II follows a peculiar development which led to the existence of self-repeating molecules able to store coded chemical information – the simplest living organisms in chemistry (how it came about we can only guess – it has been thought that the change occurred first in the peculiar soup which formed in the oceans of an Earth where there was no living matter to break down or eat up new kinds of molecule). At this point, the type of evolution which Darwin described, evolution by natural selection superimposed on the old, heart-breakingly slow process of waiting for chance hits, appeared; and *the rate of change towards new forms became vastly quicker*. Within hundreds of millions of years, molecule soup had given place to plants and animals, viruses and cucumbers, birds and termites, and finally the primate ancestors of Man.

Natural selection is the state of affairs in which there is a range of self-copying creatures which differ slightly and at random from one another, owing to minor changes in the copying 'information', and in which such minor changes are handed on to progeny. Under these circumstances, some individuals will do better than others – some changes will be favoured and others penalized. Once this basic device had got into the system of random molecular behaviour, a new order of development, the organic order, became possible and automatic, and the speed of change itself altered.

Man is the consequence of a second and equally significant breakthrough. Selection produced an animal capable of social behaviour, conceptual thought, and the transmission of experience. We can see some stages of this process in primates, and we will be discussing how it came about. Once it had come, however, we find another vast acceleration in the speed of change; living things change faster than mere inorganic accumulations, because selection reduces the random component in their behaviour. Thinking animals capable of purposive behaviour change faster still, or change their environment to suit themselves, because by thinking, and by transmitting the results of their thought in custom, literature and social practice, they perform in their heads what organisms undergoing selection have to live out at random over millennia. Moreover this kind of 'information', unlike chromosomal information, does permit the transmission of acquired characteristics – which we call experience.

Man is the outcome then of an evolution which is a logical three-tier sequence, each tier faster because less random than the one before, and he is unique, at least among the products of evolution on this planet. He lives under all three dispensations – physico-chemical in his chemistry, organic in his cellular processes, and psychosocial in his behaviour – just as he recapitulates his animal and human origins by having the same mammary glands as any mammal, and the same unconscious mental processes as an Aborigine. His evolution, if we start from scratch and hot gases, was first physical, then organic, then cultural.

There have been two critical points in evolution... The first was when, thanks to the evolution of desoxyribosenucleic acid (DNA) and genes, material organizations became self-varying and self-reproducing, and the biological phase began to operate. The second was when, thanks to the evolution of conceptual thought, symbolic language and the cumulative transmission of experience by tradition, mental or mind-accompanied organizations became self-varying and self-reproducing, and the human phase emerged. (Sir Julian Huxley)

We could go one stage further and say that yet another phase began to operate when Man learned the particular trick of checking his random or built-in mental impressions of connection, meaning and causation against the external world by the intellectual device which we call the scientific method – so that authority, tradition, magic and guess-work were replaced by a body of communicated ideas which were verifiable, evolving and capable of application to problems – from the control of smallpox to the growing of more food. It was the completion of this process, and its spread into the toughest corners of primitivism in the human mind, namely man's own self-estimate, which Darwin and Freud, among others, brought about. We are perched uneasily now on top of this colossal potential for change, with more insight than ever before into problems – such as those of our own persisting irrationality – which we can see but cannot yet control. Our task, and that of our sons, will presumably be to strike a balance between these potentials and our emotional needs, which, like our milk and our unconsciouses, are and probably always will be part of our humanness.

Since Man is now himself the subject of science, we need a science of Man. Or rather, since he has a finger in each level of evolution from chemistry to psychology, we need several. 'Anthropology', which should mean the study of Man, has been appropriated by the physical anthropologists, who study the shapes of skulls and the stature of different races, or their blood groups, and the social anthropologists, who study the custom and ways of different societies. We also need to hit the right order of magnitude – it would be a narrow business to express all human activity in terms of physical chemistry, and a rarefied one to express it in terms of psychology without reference to the brain or the body (though this is sometimes attempted). The middle order of magnitude is that of living matter, to which Man undoubtedly belongs, and this conveniently extends into chemistry on one side and behaviour on the other. This branch of science is *biology*, and human biology covers every aspect of Man from his chemical composition to his social behaviour and his mental processes, conveniently taking in on the way all the various elements which he carries with him as heirlooms from his inorganic, organic and prehuman past. That is why this is a book of human biology, and this chapter is intended to explain the choice of such a title and such a discipline as the most appropriate for the task of looking at ourselves today.

Chapter 2

Ape to Man -
Sexuality and Social Behaviour

A CENTURY ago, Charles Darwin showed us our historical continuity with animals: fifty years ago Sigmund Freud showed us that we have little insight into our own motives and mental processes. As a result of this double blow to tradition, thousands of people now know, or think they know, that Darwin proved that men are descended from apes, and Freud that everything is due to sex. The geographical and social extent of these misconceptions is itself a measure of the size of the revolution these two men brought about – the inaccuracy is a measure of the risks one runs in correcting cherished illusions.

However, the inaccuracy of the theories of monkey ancestry and sexual motivation is not as great as it looks. We will deal later with Man's probable ancestors – they were not like modern apes, but Man and ape probably had common forbears. And sexuality does indeed occupy a key place in the story of human evolution, which goes a great deal beyond its normal importance to all animals as the means by which they multiply.

If this book were about sexuality rather than about human biology it would be necessary to print many times as many copies. Sex is a matter of concern to Man. This is hardly surprising – what is more interesting is that it is a matter of anxiety. This is partly, at present, the result of patterns in our culture during the past centuries which have associated it with guilt – but why? Philosophies, religions and opinions have helped to cause or dispel anxiety about sexual matters in human cultures, but the basic liability to find sexuality disturbing, to feel anxiety about it, in a way that we do not feel anxiety about any other drive, save perhaps aggression, is very widespread in human societies.

It is a useful entry to human mental evolution and to human behaviour, to consider *why* so many societies find the organs and the phenomena associated with mating disturbing. Sex is a powerful drive – the Yoruba depict the male organ as an autonomous God of Mischief, having his own will, and the function of upsetting good order and government: we can see why. The drive to breathe, indeed, is more compulsive still, but presents no mental problems – we are not liable to be obsessed with the fear of suffocation. Sexuality involves social interaction, however – it affects our relations with others, through love, jealousy, birth and parenthood: this is the first and most obvious reason why, in social animals, it should evoke concern and caution, and this was precisely the point in primate evolution from which arose the unique and extraordinary human development of sexuality into something quite new. For it is unique, and unlike anything else in mammals – it was this, in fact, that Freud showed, though he did not himself realize the evolutionary and biological implications of his findings. Between the other primates and Man, sexuality became elaborated into a key force in shaping the development of human personality and behaviour. The only other example of a simple physiological requirement, with its associated drives, being built up in this way is found in ants and bees, where the exchange of food between individuals provided the germ from which a vast and complex social behaviour grew up. This pattern is instinctual, not social in the human sense, in that it lacks the element of learning by communication; instinct is for the ant what custom is for Man. Yet if an ant were to have a topic of anxiety, concern, expiation and ritual, one might expect it to be food and food exchange.

Man, as we have said, is a social animal – the basis of his

social behaviour is the family group, and the chief regulator of his behaviour is custom. We cannot look at Man's ancestors, save as fossils. If we look at his nearest cousins, the surviving primates, the most striking thing is the difference, not the similarity, between human and primate ways and motives in conduct.

Comparison of primate sociology with the findings (in Man)... immediately suggests a startling conclusion: the way people act, and probably have always acted, is not the expression of inherent human nature. There is a quantum difference, at points a complete opposition, between even the most rudimentary human society and the most advanced subhuman primate one. The discontinuity implies that the emergence of human society required some suppression, rather than a direct expression, of Man's primate nature. Human social life is culturally, not biologically, determined.[1]

W. H. Gilbert wrote that Man is only a monkey shaved – but the emphasis is on the shaving: the observance of convention, which is learned, rather than of monkeyness, which is built in. This is not to say that all ape and monkey behaviour is automatic, like that of ants, or that subhuman primates have no intelligence. Yet the triggers of most of their behaviour are instinctive and built-in drives and releasers of drives – these persist in Man, often where we least expect them, but they are muffled by new, social motives, which many existing mammals lack, or show only in a rudimentary form.

The start of this revolution in behaviour lies in a change affecting sexuality. Between the lower and the higher primates, the pattern of mating behaviour changed. In horses, as in many other subprimate mammals, the female experiences 'heat', a period of sexual receptivity, which is the only time when she will receive the male. Mares undergo heat soon after the birth of a foal, mate, and conceive: should they fail to conceive, heat will recur at intervals until they do so. They are then sexually 'closed' for about a year, until the foal has been born. Other mammals have different patterns of recurrence (in many it is strictly seasonal, behaviour at other times being sexless), but in almost all the female is both unreceptive and unattractive to the male when not in heat. This is the pattern in lower primates. The baboon female will mate in heat only – often with several males. At other times, males and females form one-sex groups which are sociable, but show no close male-female relationships.

At some point in primate evolution, the female became receptive all the year round and even throughout pregnancy. This apparently trifling change in behaviour was probably the trigger, or one of the triggers, which set off the evolution of Man. Between baboons and higher apes we find the effects of this change. Baboons behave very like other pack-living animals. Higher apes, with sexual activity continuing all the year round and unrelated to heat, develop a heterosexual social life which is not confined to the coital encounter; and the stimuli which set it off, while they still include such physical releasers as sight, response and odour – releasers which persist more or less strongly in Man – are no longer controlled directly by hormones, as are the brilliant buttock-patches of lower primates, which appear as a signal in the receptive individual. At the same moment, and by the same token, sex ceases to be purely reproductive in function and acquires social, psychological and recreational functions quite apart from fertility. In animals which mate at heat only, conception is the main function of mating – in animals like ourselves and the higher apes, which mate at any stage of the cycle and even during pregnancy, a high proportion of intercourse can have *no* reproductive function. Its function is social – it is an expression of 'togetherness' between mates, or of play, or of the requirement for physical pleasure.

In baboon society the key to sexual relationships is not pairing but dominance. All troop organization is based on it. The dominant males (those which by strength, cunning or size have induced the rest to accept their superiority) lead the troop when it moves – the least dominant males bring up the rear. Dominant males are most frequently groomed by females or their subordinate fellows. They choose the best food and sleeping-places. Less-dominant individuals get out of their way. The female baboon is on heat and receptive for about one week in four. With the onset of heat she leaves the all-female group and her children, and seeks out the males – in the early part of heat, the least-dominant: juveniles and subordinate adults – she is not yet 'attractive' enough to move higher. At the height of receptivity she will court a dominant male, 'presenting', grooming him, and becoming steadily more sexually attractive until, near the end of her period of oestrus, she forms for a short while a companionable pair-relation with a partner that may last hours or days – during this time, normal social behaviour is suspended. The lovers withdraw on their own. Rarely there may be fighting over one female by two males of equal dominance, yet no male, however dominant, keeps the same partner for long, or tries to monopolize more than one. Baboons have neither mates nor harems. Their sexuality is truly promiscuous, and since oestrus is suspended during pregnancy and lactation, the female baboon's love-life is restricted to a very short fraction of her total life. It is interesting to notice, however – in view of what we shall have to say later about infantile sexuality in Man – that rudimentary sex play, mounting, grooming and the like, appears well ahead of maturity. According to Sahlins 'the female higher primate is unique among female mammals in displaying the adult sexual pattern prior to puberty' – though in oestrous primates like the baboon, true oestrus does not, of course, appear until puberty itself. Sexual attractions also operate between the young, and between animals of the same sex: such subsexual activities are sociable and help to integrate the community, establish dominance patterns, and entertain the group through play.

Gorillas, by contrast, are typical higher primates. There is no troop or horde – in fact there are only a few thousand gorillas in existence. They travel in small bands, led by a 'silverback', or adult male – with him will be one or more females, children and often subordinate younger males. Over this family party the silverback rules firmly but benignly – younger males who get out of line are 'eldered' rather than attacked, and his attitude to the chastity of his females is tolerant and phlegmatic – the subordinate males are allowed their turn. (Gorillas mate rather rarely compared with many other primates.) His final sanction is not force, but a truly terrific threat display – the chest-thumping and roaring which has alarmed so many explorers is not evidence of an impending attack: a gorilla which intends to attack stares and frowns but does not roar. The spectacular tantrum is apparently for family use only.

The extended families wander over ill-demarcated territories, carrying or leading their young. Sometimes two families will join forces briefly, then separate. Gorilla life is family life, where baboon life is a little more like that of a vast institution. Even the huge silverbacks are singularly unaggressive animals. Confronted by men they cannot escape they will stare and charge, but the charge is never pressed home. It is a great disgrace among locals to be bitten by a gorilla – it proves that one panicked and ran away.

In the gibbons the analogy to Man is closer still. The normal gibbon 'social unit' consists of one male, one female and two or three offspring of different ages. There is no oestrus, so that the male's interest in his consort is continuous – the family has its 'territory', and uses its vocal powers to keep the group together, warn off others, and declare proprietorship. New families are created by the expulsion of adolescents when they reach the sexually competitive age (a most important link, as we shall see, with the factors in sexual behaviour which have contributed to the making of Man) and consequently out-breeding is the rule. The turnover of territories is high, for the gibbon, though capable of long life in captivity, does not survive very long in the wild. C. R. Carpenter[2] whose work on the gibbon is the source of our information, noted how much the gibbon family resembles that of Man.

In many primates, including monkeys, the family remains powerful even within a large troop: affection between mothers and grown-up sons and daughters is evident – a mother may even intervene to protect her grown-up son in an encounter with a more dominant male. But the nearest analogy to the human situation (no primate analogy is complete) is probably the family troop seen among gibbons.

Between the baboon and the gorilla, the change wrought by continuous receptivity has therefore taken place, and its offspring is the family or family troop, with the paterfamilias as dominant male, one or more mates, children and sometimes other related or unrelated males who share these mates but do not challenge the senior male's ascendancy, or who are driven away when they do. With this change comes another. The baby baboon is 'brought up' by one parent only. It is born with a developed musculature, for the troop moves and there is no time for it to learn to cling onto the mother's hair – it has to be born with a cling reflex fully and functionally developed. At first contact between mother and child is continual by day and night. Experiments with dummy 'mothers' have shown that this contact, in which the soft texture of maternal fur is a more potent factor than her status as a source of food, plays a big part in the emotional development of the baby monkey. This relationship is intensive but short – within a relatively short time the baby begins to ride instead of clinging, to leave the mother for longer and longer periods, and soon after weaning it is able to forage for itself. At first it returns to the 'softness' of the mother for reassurance, especially if frightened or puzzled, but soon its life shifts to the play-group of youngsters and its climb to its place in the dominance-hierarchy of the troop begins.

In the higher apes, by contrast, birth takes place at a far less advanced stage of development, and maternal dependence is far longer. The mother still occupies the main place in the infant's life, for she carries, nurses, grooms and disciplines it – but it has contact also with adult males, though there is no true sharing of domestic duties, such as we see in some pair-mating birds. In Man, the immaturity at birth is still more pronounced – as pronounced as in the kitten, which is born blind and helpless; this dependence period is not only longer in proportion to the lifespan – it is biologically prolonged, to give a period of true, parent-dependent childhood by a peculiarity of the human growth and development curve. After a rather rapid epoch of development and growth which leaves the human child, at about its fifth year, walking, talking and weaned, but still wholly unable to fend for itself, the curve flattens out. Growth progresses at a slower tempo, until just before puberty, when it undergoes a spurt. Full size, sexual maturity, and adult intelligence are then reached relatively quickly. It is as though a 'shelf' or plateau had been inserted into the human growth curve, so as to lengthen childhood disproportionately. Traces of this shelf can be seen in lower primate growth curves, but its full development is seen only in Man.

We now have two attributes of higher primates which distinguish them from lower primates, and both of these are accentuated in Man: continuous female receptivity, leading to pairing (not necessarily one to one) and family-group formation; and prolonged parental dependence. The third such attribute has already been mentioned – the reduction in purely biological, 'trigger' type controls on sexual behaviour, such as heat, appearance of coloured patches, or of characteristic signal-behaviour, without which the male is not excited to mate – and the substitution, in all known human societies, of *social* and customary controls. Of these the most widespread is the rule of exogamy – of avoiding sexual contacts with parents, and usually with sibs. These avoidances are almost universal in human social custom, but they are not 'instinctive', as the male baboon's avoidance of the non-oestrous female is instinctive, for despite the cultural prohibition, sex play between immature brothers and sisters, and even sex relations between adult sibs, occur clandestinely and not uncommonly in most cultures, and parent-child sex relations, chiefly between father and daughter, are far from rare though they are execrated. Herein lies the difference between a built-in and a social mechanism. It was Sigmund Freud who first recognized the importance of the human fear and detestation of incest – we do not fear and prohibit things we have no biological drive to do, we fear and prohibit things we *have* a biological drive to do, but which the cultural tradition rejects. Why does it reject it? The rejection is so built-in to most of us that prior to Freud's question, most people would have answered 'because it is unnatural, and only depraved individuals would do such a thing'. Others might have seen in our exogamy the accumulated wisdom of Man, which had discovered the ill effects of inbreeding – no doubt an incidental evolutionary advantage would come from whatever it was that made us exogamous, but this is not the whole answer. Avoidance of incest is not instinctive. Yet something built-in appears to favour it, just as something built-in makes sex a sensitive subject for Man. In fact the two 'somethings' appear to be identical – they are part of the mental configuration which has both produced and been produced by the changes in sexual behaviour which separate Man from other primates. This crucial matter, the development of human sociality and personality, had been touched on by Darwin when he described the physical sequence of changes from primate ancestor to Man. In some ways he came remarkably near to Freud's eventual answers. That he did not go further is partly due to the fact that, unlike those who came after the revolution which he made, Darwin had not himself had time to adjust emotionally and intellectually to his own discoveries. The emotive side is important in this context, because of the feedback system which exists, and must be overcome, when Man studies Man's mental reactions. These mental reactions, as we shall see, were by their nature anxiety-producing and 'rejected' – the rejection of them is built-in by evolution. In other words, the matter which had to be exposed in understanding the structure of human sexuality and personality is uniquely able to upset our judgment because, being human, we have to use the mechanisms we are studying. This poses a problem in scientific argument which is new, quantitatively if not qualitatively, because we have to recognize the fact of so-called 'resistance', which we can easily verify in our own experience, and which makes it as hard for some people to consider the relevant ideas as it would be for them to see into their own ears. At the same time, we have to refrain from using this as an argument on theoretical questions, because it is obviously the joker to end all rational discussion.

Let us now try and fit Darwin and Freud together and see what the speculative structure looks like.

Darwin published the *Descent of Man* in 1871 – thirteen years after the *Origin*. The whole of the evolutionary argument except the explicit application to Man was really present in the earlier book. The full title of the new work was *The Descent of Man, and selection in relation to sex*. The second part of the title actually accounts for more than half the text, and deals with a matter which, though Darwin does relate it to Man, is not a primary argument in his theory of human origins. It was some-thing arising out of his general evolutionary theory which had been criticized, and this second book was an opportunity to deal with it at greater length. The juxtaposition of sexual selection and human descent seems therefore to have been a matter of convenience rather than relationship.

We read *The Descent* now, of course, with hindsight, and much of the argument for human evolution is familiar. In these days it is perhaps the part which dates more which we can read with greatest profit – the argument about the evolution of the higher faculties and the human sense of values. One of the privileges of our hindsight is that we can see how Darwin handles Freud's material but skirts round his interpretation of it. In his discussion of human behaviour Darwin relates the evolution of morals to family-situation, and reaches as it were the edge of the super-ego concept. But much more striking, of course, to a Freudian hindsight is the accident which sets this sort of argument side by side with the discussion of sexual dimorphism. I would not venture to suggest that Darwin was unconsciously aware of a relationship between them (if he had been, he would have been much more likely to avoid the subject altogether), but the fact remains that we now read as a unified argument something which he intended to take in two little-connected subjects.

The implications of sexual dimorphism – of the fact that there are obvious anatomical differences between male and female – are critical to Freud's account of human development. In the event, Darwin tries to explain the significance of sexual dimorphism in general, but Freud explains the application of Darwin's selectionist argument to human socio-ethical behaviour, the point which Darwin was looking for but did not quite find. With this in mind we can relate the two. We shall find that not only Darwin but Freud gains in the process.

Darwin's great fundamental discovery was the idea of natural selection. It followed from this idea that any clear trend or development in form was likely to be in some way adaptive.

In some animal species, cock and hen for example, there is a striking difference between the sexes – sometimes an exorbitant one, like the clumsy, two-foot-long tail of the male quetzal, which can barely fly in mating plumage. In others, such as penguins or gulls, the sexes appear identical. Why did selection favour these differences, and in some species only? The point long worried Darwin – it underlies the remark in one of his letters that the eye no longer troubled him, but the sight of a peacock's feather made him feel sick.

His eventual explanation was two-pronged. Some of the instances represent different functions in upbringing. If men must work and women must weep, or rather suckle, one would expect this to be reflected anatomically. Others, like the peacock's tail and the stag's antlers, it was reasonable to explain as a means of competition between males by which the most vigorous would have the most progeny – either through ability to attract females and keep them attracted, or through the ability to fight rivals and monopolise the most desirable mates.

Darwin's view of sexual ornament is that in Man and in animals it is chiefly competitive. But since his time interest has shifted to a related function of sexual dimorphism – its use in recognition. In territory-keeping birds, the cock drives off other cocks – often without actually fighting them – by displaying his markings and song against theirs. There are occasional violent encounters, but as a rule territories tend to subsist automatically by a form of behavioural agreement, based on the use of these signal mechanisms.

In gulls which do not have visibly different sexes, the signal is the adoption of a particular posture. The cock bird defending his territory takes up a threat posture – if the intruder is also a cock, he will retaliate or retreat, but a hen will carry out an appeasement display, taking up a posture as different as possible from the threat position.

This meets the need to distinguish a potential, or an accepted, mate or mates from an intruder. The other tolerated parties on a territory are the young. These are usually protected from being driven away prematurely by the fact that the behaviour or markings which trigger the aggressive response of the parents do not appear until sexual maturity. This is necessary in species where parental dependence goes on until the young are as big as the adults. In other species, there are precautions to keep the young away from an aggressive parent. Though brown bears are commonly monogamous, cubs never see their father, and are not deserted by the mother until they are big enough to climb out of his reach. Young male Northern fur seal live with the cows until shortly after spermatogenesis begins, when they go off alone and do not return until they have rapidly grown enough muscle to take place in the dominance-order of males. In general, a long-term family-situation in pair-mating animals has two requirements – that other sexually active individuals should be driven away, either from a territory or from the female, and that the young and the accepted mate should not.

Freud had little Darwinian background. His only obvious debt to Darwin is the idea of a primal horde in which the strongest male ruled. But it was an important debt, because it started him with a firmly Darwinian idea that sexual dimorphism was primarily competitive. He did not, however, really apply the selectionist argument to his central and most surprising finding

– the nature of the anxiety behind the human fear of incest, an anxiety which seems in many ways to have dominated human social development, the so-called castration fear. This was an empirical observation which he had great difficulty in explaining – and, as Darwin had to invent the idea of pangenesis because he had not seen the work of Mendel, so Freud was obliged to turn to racial memory to account for something which makes sense in evolutionary terms but in virtually no others.

Freud found that in his patients, conscious behaviour, normal and abnormal, was influenced by thought-patterns which were unconscious and followed characteristic non-rational sequences. Much of their content was sexual, and seemed to date from early childhood, and there was an extremely powerful block to making conscious its original significance.

The imagery showed an extraordinary preoccupation with the external genitalia, with fantasies of incest, and with fantasies of castration. This system of unconscious imagery and associated anxieties Freud called the Oedipus complex – after the Greek hero who inadvertently killed his father, married his mother, and blinded – or castrated – himself in expiation. It appeared to date from a particular period in childhood, between the ages of four and six, and the associations behind it were remarkably consistent, one of the chief components being intense anxiety over the difference between the sexes, combined, in the male child, with a fear of injury to his own genitalia. The female organs were a particular focus of this anxiety. They seemed to be interpreted as a wound or mutilation which was in itself threatening. The male child apparently saw them as threat of castration, while the female child came to think of herself as actually deprived of a male organ.

Freud was as impressed as we are by the oddity of this at first sight, but once he had recognized the irrational train of thought behind it, it became obvious that there were echoes of it all over human behaviour, custom and literature, which become progressively more striking as we get used to the peculiar kind of non-conceptual association which determines unconscious imagery. The outburst of anxiety appeared to be connected with another mechanism which Freud had been obliged to postulate – the sexual attraction of the male child to its mother, and its resentment toward, and fear of reprisals from, the father.

Given the existence of infantile sexuality, which was perhaps the most biologically surprising part of the story, it seemed reasonable that the sexual object for a male child should be the mother, and that the father should be felt as a rival. But where did the fear of castration come from? It was important, because it seemed to be the driving-force behind the peculiar human incest-anxiety and behind the adult behaviour-disorders Freud was investigating.

Freud at first attributed it to injudicious threats from parents, and wondered whether he might not himself be suggesting it inadvertently to adults during treatment. But it became clear that where there had been threats these only aggravated a fear already present, which seemed to appear spontaneously at the appropriate age.

It was found in children who had never been threatened, children who had no parents, and in places where the psycho-analyst could not possibly have put it, from Greek mythology to *Tristram Shandy* – in the impolite ballad, for example, which gave us the phrase 'pull Devil, pull baker' and which repeats the typical concerns verbatim, even down to the interpretation of the vulva as a castrating wound, turning them to reassuring mockery.

There are two obvious biological comments at this point. Both have already been made by the psychoanalyst Fenichel. The first is that the Oedipal responses not only have every appearance of being in some way built in, but that they look uncommonly like a temporary organ with a function. The second is that sexuality, in its biological as well as its conversa-tional sense, is a correlate of reproduction. The mention of infantile sexuality at once calls for some explanation of what sexuality is doing in infancy. Some infant animals show minor sexual reflexes, such as erectility, but well-developed sexual drives in infancy would be an example of what is called anticipation, and this kind of shift makes one look for a possible adaptation of an old mechanism to a new function.

Freud did in fact recognize the Oedipal reactions as being built-in. The tendency of his time would have been to label them instinctive, but this Freud would not do. Not, curiously enough, because of the extreme difficulty of justifying alleged human instincts, and the uncertainty how much any built-in response owes to shared experience, but because he had throughout life a fixed idea that there could be two human instincts and two only – the two posts were held by different candidates at different points in his career, but at that time both were occupied. Instead he turned to the idea of racial memory. The fear of castration was quite irrelevant to any known human society, but it might not always have been. All these anxieties must be echoes from the fiercer and nastier days of the primal horde, where the sons had to kill their father in order to possess his wives. We find him wondering if there were really times when sons risked castration, or whether the threat was enough (a biologically sensible comment, for in animals, unlike pugnacious Man, the threat, being economical of life, nearly always *is* enough – witness the chest thumping of the gorilla, which is sheer bluff).

We need not bother now with racial memory – evolutionary 'memory' in the genes is a fully adequate explanation. If human sexuality had been 'brought forward' into pre-reproductive life, as it apparently has been, the Oedipal reactions with their peculiar anxieties and their genital content could be part of the shift. Is there any other peculiarity of human development compared with that of other primates which makes such a shift likely? In fact there is – the conspicuous split in the growth curve which we have already mentioned, due to a plateau of retarded development put, between the fifth and ninth years, bodily into the smooth growth-curve typical of subprimate mammals. The development which in other mammals is continuous is in Man split into two – an early phase up to the age of five, then a long period of marking time, and then the pre-pubertal growth spurt and the appearance of the secondary sex characters. The two peaks of psychosexual development in Freud's theory therefore fit neatly over two periods of active development in other fields, and impulses towards sexual expression, male avoidance and so forth, which might logically be expected in a competing mammal just before puberty, could well have been split off and pushed into infancy, where their functions, if any, would have to be very different indeed, and concerned with parent-child relationships, which are the chief social concerns at that age.

It has been realized before that 'castration anxiety', which has every appearance of fulfilling a special function, but which seems inappropriate to the childhood situation in any known human society, would be much less so if it occurred in an animal which had no lag-period; it could then represent an adaptation which protected immature males over the awkward age between sexing and achieving competitive size. If there was no lag-period in Man, puberty would be complete about the age of nine. The timing of the Oedipal reactions (four to six years) would there-fore still put them well ahead of the probable age of appearance of secondary sex-characters; more recent workers have put them if anything earlier still. But Freudian experience has always insisted that the onset of 'castration anxiety' is in some way triggered by the recognition of the genitalia themselves. This is possibly an important clue to its origins. The timing and content of the reaction in Man would be intelligible if it evolved originally (a) among pair-mating animals (b) with prolonged and lengthening maternal dependence (c) where instead of the secondary sex characters the genitalia themselves had recently become the primary sex signals, so that males became competi-tive long before they were mature. This might happen as a by-product of quite unconnected changes (in posture or hair density, for example) or even of an interference between grow-ing intelligence, which associated male genitalia with male secondary sex characters, and instinct, which excited hostility to them. It would call for a major adaptation in behaviour to maintain the family-pattern, if young males had to love their mother in order to stay with her, but avoid her as a sex object, so as not to be chased off the territory. Avoidance of the sexually displaying female as a 'castration threat', and mixed feelings towards the adult male in which his genitalia served as a dominance-signal, could serve to keep young males out of the competitive situation while still maternally dependent.

Our guess, then – and it can be no more than a guess – is that at some point in primate evolution there arose a risk of a clash between the need for young males to stay within the family group, and the persisting sexual dominance of the father; this might be due to earlier 'recognition' of maleness, or, quite possibly, to the very displacement of sexual behaviour into prepuberty which we see in other primates (chiefly, among living apes, in females, a fact which may be significant, for the living apes have bypassed this particular biological problem – that may be the reason that they diverged from the line of human development). No living ape has quite the right ingredients for the mixture this theory needs – baboons show much dominance, but the dominant male does not monopolize mates – only their most exciting moments: gorilla paterfamilias is firm with the young, but does not object to their mating with his females.

The hypothesis demands that somewhere in primate lineage the requisite explosive mixture should have appeared, or begun to appear – we do not see it in modern primates for the reason which ensures that '*missing links*' are missing: they were unstable equilibria, 'prohibited' because they would have disrupted the behaviour of the species – they were selected against or steered round, and the evolution of the highly unusual pattern in Man probably reflects the steering-round process. It also answers Freud's questions about 'racial memory' and whether there ever was a time when primate males threatened to castrate their sons – almost certainly there was not, the steering-round process having been brought about because families in which such tendencies appeared would have had poor survival value. Some have argued that in modern monkeys the Oedipal situation of avoidance for the dominant male is lifelong – certainly it has been observed that if a young male is repeatedly worsted in this way when attempting to mate he may be behaviourally castrated and become scared of the female's approaches as productive only of assault from male superiors.

One cannot say that the hypothesis I have put forward here is right. Nobody should quote it in any examination as fact. What does seem likely is that if this hypothesis is wrong, something rather like it is right; at least, a study of human custom, psychoanalytic data, (where dominance as well as sexuality can be detected in our anxiety-patterns – this is the resolution of the Freud-Adler dispute) and primate behaviour strongly suggest such a guess as I have made. Not all of us can listen in to psychoanalytic sessions, but all of us can read literature, and there is something in the remark that the best evidence for Freud is that he makes intelligible sense of *Tristram Shandy*. We have very scanty, though increasing, data about the behaviour of big primates in the wild – watching them requires much time and trouble. At what point the crucial development is likely to have occurred we cannot really do more than guess – it must have been somewhere after childhood began to lengthen and sexual behaviour moved forward into infancy. Perhaps, as we have said, the gibbons come closest to our own pattern. Unfortunately our primate ancestors are not now available for inspection – the development may have been very early, or relatively late; among animals more like lemurs than apes, or among the just pre-human protoanthropoids of the very early pliocene.

Freud's original interest as a doctor lay in psychopathology, though to study it he was obliged to uncover the normal sources of character-structure in Man.

Perhaps the oddest biological feature of human psychosexual development is its surprising and un-Darwinian vagueness of aim. Fixity of sexual object, at least to the extent of mating with a potentially fertile female, would seem to be the behavioural minimum to be expected in a system where 'fitness' is a correlate, simply, of total fertile progeny; the nadir of unfitness is inability or unwillingness to breed. But the human sexual object is not fixed – under present conditions at least, it is rather easily displaced.

Not only is there a large variation, both personal and social, in what female attributes attract the male – there are also gross diversions of sex drive away from its biological object, to inappropriate objects – members of the same sex, articles of clothing, particular rituals or conditions, inanimate objects, which, for the unfortunate individual so afflicted, are as compulsively attractive as the normal female is to most men. The majority of these deviations occur in males. Now and then a culture develops one of them as an acceptable sexual vehicle – as ancient Greece encouraged homosexual relations between men and boys. Under such conditions many people – all those who can – will exhibit the behaviour. In cultures which disapprove of such activities, only those will who must, because they cannot help it. This suggests that such emphases are present in embryo in many of us, but that in some individuals they take over from normal sex with the force of instinct, though they are not 'instinctive' in any true sense. Thus in our culture, we find women with long hair beautiful, but a minority of individuals have their whole sexual impulse directed toward the hair, not the woman.

These deviations, paraphilias or fetishes, are held by Freudians to reflect persisting infantile anxiety, which still sees the female as a threat-situation to be avoided: the sex drive will out, however, and has to be channelled away from her towards something irrelevant. For the biologist, however, such uncertainty of aim is most odd – it runs wholly counter to what we find in animals, where although maternal responses can be imprinted in birds so that they treat a cardboard box as their mother, sexual behaviour is of the lock and key variety; this is what Darwinism would lead one to expect.

Almost all such displacements reduce their possessor's reproductive effectiveness, and many prevent mating altogether. According to Freud, the liability to these deviations is a direct hazard of the Oedipal processes, and of the need, effectively, to reverse or overcome the avoidance of the female before adult reproduction becomes possible. Persistence of this anxiety may divert the sexual drive away from its proper target and dissipate it on an irrelevant one – a member of the same sex, an inappropriate part of the body, or an inanimate object.

There is more, in all probability, to the biology of paraphilias than this – one was recently excised surgically, along with a temporal lobe epileptogenic focus – but they set essentially the same evolutionary problem whatever their cause. The human pattern of development carries, empirically, a sizeable risk of interference with eventual mating. There is a strong temptation to apply here what Prof J. B. S. Haldane once called Pangloss' theorem.

Voltaire's Dr Pangloss believed that 'everything is for the best in the best of all possible worlds'.

According to Pangloss, if everything is for the best in the best of selectionist worlds, the peculiar mode of human sexual development must involve some overriding gain to the species; if not, it would have disappeared, or at least become reliable. This is a fallacy. Natural selection responds; it does not plan, though when equilibria shift it will compensate. The psycho-sexual pattern in Man looks very much like the end-product of a biological emergency. The castration-fear is not, for example, sex-limited; instead, it is developed in the female into a rather cumbersome mechanism of 'cryptandric' behaviour by which the male is helped, as it were, in reversing his responses and reaching the adult pattern. The untidiness of this seems typical of the evolutionary 'demon' making do. At the same time there is this much validity in the Panglossian argument; where a swing of this kind opens a new possibility, selection may exploit and expand it.

The Oedipal responses may carry an inherent risk of

interference with eventual reproduction, but their persistence suggests a new adaptive function in their new situation. It seems reasonable to suggest that this function is morphogenetic, and that they have been positively selected because of their effects on human mental and social development. It is not impossible that by necessitating repression and a mind divided actively into conscious and unconscious levels they produced the most significant adaptation in mammalian history, the emergence of conceptual thought.

Quite apart from all this, the widespread use which primate societies make of 'loose' sexual feeling, to cement one-sex groups, to create dominance-patterns, and for purposes of play, makes one wonder whether the ability to switch sexual empathy from mating into other contexts, such as homosexual friendship cemented by sex play between males, or object-interest in non-sexual things, may not have had important social uses in human and prehuman development. The potentiality for quasi-sexual attachments with members of the same sex is general in Man; the 'homosexual' is abnormal, not in showing it, but in having his heterosexual drives poorly developed or blocked. Had the prehuman male concentrated his affection on the female alone, human families might have remained of gorilla size, and the formation of hunting and war-parties of males, with corporate all-male rituals, such as we see in many tribal societies, might never have taken place. Argument about what is or is not acceptable or 'moral' in our own developed society has often misled investigators studying a subject so emotive as sex. Most of the activities which past generations have stigmatized as perverse or unnatural have a place in mammalian behaviour and in most of our minds. They are part of the sexual behaviour of the species, and the ability to display them, though, when it is overdeveloped, it may hinder reproduction, may still have had secondary social consequences which have strongly favoured human adaptability and social behaviour. Even schizophrenic behaviour, which we now recognize as a grave disability and a frank disease, is made use of by primitive societies – individuals who can 'dissociate' in this way, and make the unconscious fears and drives of the society conscious, have a place in ritual and in priestcraft which, for the society as a whole, may be therapeutic.

It is very dangerous to base elaborate argument about Man on Darwinian indirect selection, but we need not do so, for in Man, as sexual behaviour passed from purely hormonal to social control, new types of fitness emerged in which the selecting mechanisms were themselves social. It is probably true that we are as we are because we developed as we did.

Mammalian residues still persist in human sexuality, and we may underrate them. Blushing, and the interest of some individuals in the reddening of the buttocks produced by whipping, may contain echoes of the 'releaser' sex skin of lower primates. The sexual function of odour, which is highly important in most mammals, is a case in point. Olfactory stimuli in sex are repressed or repudiated in our culture, but not in all, and many individuals are aware of them. Freud's follower Groddeck thought that 'in matters of love we let our noses decide for us' and taught that the loss of olfactory acuity between dog and Man is due to infantile repression, not to physiology – a gross overstatement, perhaps, but one which raises interesting questions. It also illustrates the extreme difficulty of studying human variability. In our culture some individuals can detect, and are excited by, specifically sexual odours – others do not seem to detect them, yet others are repelled by them. In a lower mammal there would be a lock-and-key effect, stimulus producing excitement, or stimulus producing repulsion. In Man, other forces, childhood experience, repression, conditioning, social custom (French literature exploits and recognizes the erotic aspects of body odour – English and American do not) and possibly genetic variation all play a part. Added to this, many people can react as strongly to a *conditioned* stimulus of this kind – the odour of tobacco, or of rubber contraceptives – as a mammal does to its fixed 'releaser'. One might be tempted to say that the original mammalian mechanism is defunct, and any hints of its persistence are accidental. Yet it has been shown that the inability of men to smell a material (exaltolide) which is chemically similar to the sex releaser of deer and musk rats, can be reversed by estrogens, while the ability of women to smell it varies during the menstrual cycle. This is an instructive and typical instance. Most of the lower primate releasers probably do persist in Man, either in a muffled form, or possibly in certain individuals only – but all such physiological automation has been overlaid in sexual behaviour by the vast psychological and social superstructure which is characteristic of human sexuality. The move is constantly away from the purely auto-matic towards the socially-conditioned.

Returning to the so-called 'deviations' of human sexual behaviour – its compulsive diversion, that is, into non-repro-ductive and apparently inappropriate channels, there is another, though highly speculative, consequence of what we have said concerning the human growth curve which ought to be men-tioned here. It is an old and consoling idea, discredited largely by modern studies, that such deviations, especially those of which society disapproves, are 'constitutional', and due to built-in physical causes. This is almost certainly not true for most of them – predominant homosexuals are not a physical 'third sex', nor have they inappropriate chromosomes or hor-mones. Strangest of all, the sex role in Man, male or female, with all the social and sexual behaviour attached thereto, is *learned* – a child brought up for the first five years in the 'wrong' sex role will have great difficulty in reversing it to agree with his or her physical structure. This tells in favour of early experience rather than physical make-up as a cause of aberrant sexual behaviour, but it does not rule out the idea that given the same conditions some people may be more susceptible than others. We find the same thing when we examine the other conse-quences of 'immaturity' – the persistence into adult life of patterns which ought, according to Freud, to have been lost in infancy. A very few of us keep our thymus glands instead of losing them. Some of us keep our Oedipal fears. Just as some people, exposed to tubercle germs, catch the disease, while others do not, so some children with disturbed childhoods show the predicted difficulties while others do not. The gross disturbances of sexual behaviour which handicap some people are good material for this kind of study, for they are both evident and, apparently, biologically patterned, and some, as we have said, show evidence of cerebral localization – of structural trouble, that is, in definite parts of the brain.

Kallmann (1952) found that identical twins are more like in this, as in every other, investigated respect than are fraternal twins. This means little, but there may, and some would say there must, be some 'constitutional' factors behind such behaviour disorders, at least within a given culture pattern. Consideration of this in Darwin's terms has led Hutchinson (1959) to make an important suggestion – the first I have mentioned here which is directly open to experiment. If any hereditary factor regularly predisposed to paraphilia severe enough to block reproduction, there should be heavy selection against it. Hutchinson has attempted to guess what kind of physical trait might have this effect, and asks whether constitutional differences between normal and abnormal psychosexual development may not depend on individual differences of development rate.

There are in fact, as we have seen, strong reasons for associating rate-determining mechanisms with the way in which human sexuality has evolved – it arises, apparently, from a shift in the early scale of growth time. Some of the most critical processes apparently fall at a point in the growth curve where, owing to its shape, a small change in contributing rates might produce a very large change in the duration of a 'temporary organ', by moving it, like the bubble in the spirit-level, along the entire extent of the 'plateau'. A difference of rate, heritable or otherwise, which displaced the Oedipal behaviour by six months in an animal whose curve was continuous might shift it in Man by several years, and make it persist throughout the whole of the lag-phase – during which, presumably, attitudes and behavioural patterns are hardening.

In fact, the single piece of relevant evidence about a relation between timing and mental health is negative – in children with constitutional precocious puberty, whose growth curve is continuous like that in sheep, and who have no lag-period, physical puberty is complete at six to eight years, but there is said to be no parallel acceleration in mental, sexual, or – oddly enough – dental development.

Environmental effects on psychosexual development are usually discussed in terms of 'traumatic' experience, with much less attention to the additional possibility of direct physical retardation. Greenacre (1953, 1955) found that the early traumatic experience in paraphilics was often an illness between the second and fourth year. Illness and separation from parents may indeed be psychical stresses, but, particularly in children, where emotion itself affects appetite, they produce physical checking as well. The effects of such checks to growth in size in young humans and animals are usually made good by the 'post-inhibitory growth rebound', but this may not restore a completely normal balance, or deal with any discrepancies which have arisen in physical development. If emotional stresses upset our development, as we know they do, the upset must be mediated either through mental changes, or through physical, or – since mind and body are one system – far more probably through both. It is an idea worth investigating.

We can see the outlines of the process by which primate sexuality changed into human sociality, but not the detail. On this one might speculate indefinitely – that the need to repress so much early experience into the 'dream time' may have freed the consciousness to think in the straight lines characteristic of human conceptual thought, instead of the crooked lines of perceptual thinking which we find in the unconscious mind. There is the phenomenon of over-compensation – whereby frustration, and especially, some would say, sexual frustration, may make an individual transcend himself. There is the effect of unconscious forces, not only in making us unable to see the obvious, which is a handicap, but in predisposing us to see the unobvious, which may make us geniuses. Darwin and Freud, like the rest of us, probably owed their unusual insights to peculiarities of personality which arose in their infancy, probably from psychosexual causes. The results were as beneficial to Man the species as any mutation. It appears that the human mind, unwieldy and unreliable as it may appear when we consider the unconscious forces at work on it, is actually a more valuable matrix of ideas and inspiration precisely for that reason, for pure reason would be unmotivated save by idle curiosity. Curiosity is an important enough motive in primates as well as in Man, but it lacks the force of drives originating in the unconscious. By making us liable to built-in discontents the 'dream time' gives us art and the raw material of discovery, namely originality. The knack which science has brought us is of comparing these inspirations with reality. It is not unduly arrogant to see this, perhaps, as the summit of primate development, in which, in the words of Prof Dobzhansky, 'biological evolution has transcended itself'.

Chapter 3

Ape to Man -
Tools, Fossils and Agriculture

WE HAVE seen how the peculiarities of primate sexual behaviour, the lengthening of childhood, the growth of brain size and of intelligence, and the development of social and manipulative skills have all taken part in the composition of what we now call specifically human behaviour. But how these changes were related to time, and to the physical and anatomical evolution of Man, is largely an open question. We have no access to our ancestors and we never can have – the most we have is fossils. But, as Prof Sherwood L. Washburn put it, 'our ancestors were not fossils, they were striving creatures...what evolved was the pattern of life of intelligent, exploratory, playful, vigorous primates'.[3] One can draw some conclusions about them from their bones, but one could be wrong. If we had never seen a chimp, only a chimp skull, would we be able to be sure chimps could not talk? Attempts have been made to teach them, but with no success beyond the one word 'cup' in one individual chimp – their brain is not organized for speech. From the antiquity of certain lines alive today we can infer that the lengthening of childhood, which begins in the higher apes, is old. So is the drive towards bipedal walking – a very important skill, which gives the power of endurance in travel. A chimp can outrun a man, but not outwalk him. Much, much later, we can infer that creatures which bury their dead with grave-goods, or make rock-paintings, must have had a complex system of belief and custom. In between the two, we can identify fire from ashes, tools from their presence and marks on other objects, and hunting from the bones of the animals killed. But we cannot know our ancestors more intimately than that – save that we have some access to their ways of thinking from residues of those ways in our own minds.

The question 'What is Man?' has been asked by philosophers and others in a good many contexts which have bent the significance of the enquiry: for us it is an important question in a strictly practical context. We have a range of fossils – mostly skulls – which can now be dated with fair accuracy, and go back about a million years. The oldest are decidedly ape-like; the youngest are indistinguishable from the bones of our neighbours today. Now the bones of a chimpanzee, had we never seen a live one, are a fair parody of a human skeleton, though from their detail we could infer that the way of chimp life was very different from ours – arboreal, not upright, using the teeth to fight and gnaw, and from the brain impression of a really good skull we might perhaps infer that chimpanzees do not talk. Somewhere in the sequence from ape-like to man-like, there must have appeared a creature recognizably human, or at least an ape-like man who was rather more than a man-like ape. Semantic squabbles apart, what are we going to take as the criteria of Man?

One might incline to choose speech, but this is one power one cannot really infer with certainty from fossils. Another of the most popular criteria in the past, the making and use of tools, has now been badly shaken by the discovery of primitive tools in association with the bones of primates which could not in any other sense be regarded as regular men – small-brained, not-fully-upright pre-men with brains no bigger than those of modern apes. Darwin had guessed, with some plausibility, that to use tools one would need to walk habitually on two feet, without needing hand-support, and that once tool using began, the drive to bipedalism would be hastened; in this view the sequence of progress would be – partly erect posture – power to use tools – fully bipedal stance – better tools – premium on higher intelligence – further progress. It now looks as if this is correct: the tools came first, and the power to make them may have influenced the process of evolving human structure and human abilities from a much earlier stage than had been thought.

All of us have seen some pictures somewhere of the skull sequence – longer now than in Darwin or Haeckel's time, but in some ways not much clearer – over which such bitter dispute raged between those who asserted the evolution of Man on scientific grounds and those who denied it on religious. It was argued that the aberrant skulls, not Man, not ape, with heavy brow ridges but big brains, were those of abnormals 'turned out to die' by human communities (in contradiction of the fact that no abnormal man with such attributes had ever been reported). Fortunately for science, which might have been badly shaken by a débacle over a cherished specimen, one of the skulls most convenient to old theories of anthropogenesis, and increasingly inconvenient to modern ones, 'Piltdown Man', only turned out to be a fraud when the issue of human evolution had moved beyond the reach of reasonable dispute. Modern dating methods, which exposed this hoax, also serve to dispose of the 'freak' theory, if it persisted – and in any case, whole populations of such 'freaks' with their tools and their food remains are now known.

The history of these fossils extends over four great Ice Ages – possibly more: the first such Ice Age was at its height about 550,000 years ago, the next some 400,000, the next just under 200,000, and the last a mere 50,000. The oldest tools seem to date from shortly before the first of these ice ages. They are associated in time with the highest man-apes rather than the most ancient men.

Next to tool-using, and associated with it, true bipedality seems to be a test of Man, and, from what we have said about tool-making by pre-men, a far better one. Man is a walker – apes are food-gatherers, as are some men, but men are also hunters, and to hunt one must give up the slow and shambling

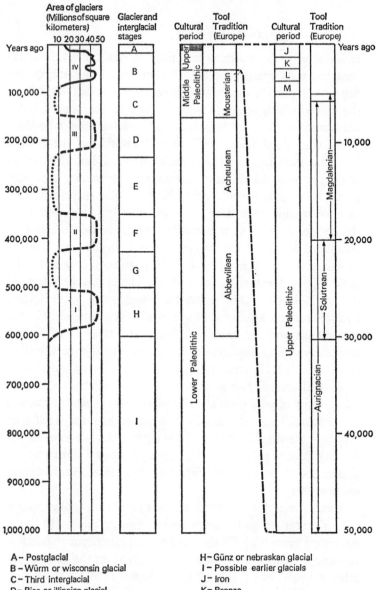

Area of glaciers (Millions of square kilometers)

Glacier and interglacial stages

Cultural period

Tool Tradition (Europe)

A – Postglacial
B – Würm or wisconsin glacial
C – Third interglacial
D – Riss or illinoian glacial
E – Second or 'great' interglacial
F – Mindel or kansan glacial
G – First interglacial

H – Günz or nebraskan glacial
I – Possible earlier glacials
J – Iron
K – Bronze
L – Neolithic
M – Mesolithic

FIG. 2.—Time-scale correlating periods and tool traditions with the four great glaciations of the Pleistocene epoch. Glacial advances and retreats shown by solid black curve are accurately known; those shown by broken curve are less certain; those shown by dotted curve are uncertain. Columns at far right show an expanded view of last 50,000 years on two centre columns.

mode of progress which puts a hand to the ground now and then, and walk upright and far. The evidence for walking power depends on parts of the skeleton other than the skull –especially the pelvis, which becomes a 'basin' to hold the organs, not a coathanger to suspend them from. The ancient men who lived in the Old World from the First to the middle of the Fourth Ice Ages were human-type, bipedal walkers, and also skilled hunters, who could kill large animals, as evidenced by the bones found in their household rubbish. They also made fire, had tools of traditional pattern, and had already passed well into the region of cultural transmission which is the true test of completed Man. Still earlier pre-men had already lost the hefty canine teeth typical of apes, and the huge shoulders and bull-necks which went with them. Brow ridges too had already become reduced – this, it has been suggested, by Prof Curt Richter, reflects a process of increasing social affability and a cultural discount on rage and dominance exemplified by the gorilla's scowling-display; his argument was that in selecting tame and biddable farm animals we have selected individuals with small adrenal glands (this is obvious if one tries to handle the progeny of wild mice after handling tame laboratory mice), and that small adrenals go with less rugged features. That is as may be – the rugged male gorilla is a gentle soul *en famille*, and uses his famous rages solely for display purposes. Perhaps with greater social co-operation big bones and big adrenals became less necessary.

A man, then, for our purposes, is a tool-using walker with a cultural tradition and a brain bigger than an ape's. He needs the bigger brain both for the cultural and intelligent activities – learning, speech and the like – which give him the edge on all other animals, but also for the development of his tool-using capacity, for this depends on manual dexterity, and dexterity in turn upon the way the skin and muscles are represented on the surface of the brain. Compared with lower primates, human brains devote a large amount of space to the motor and sensory wiring of the thumb and hand, and also, significantly, of the lips, tongue, pharynx and other organs of speech – the two skills, manual and communicative, seem to have come roughly together. It is pretty certain that hunters as proficient as Pekin Man could talk to each other, even if their topics of conversation were limited.

Yet another truly human character, related again to this question of brain size, is inordinately long childhood. By walking upright women lost the monkey's ability to produce relatively big-headed babies (some mothers have trouble even with the present human size) through narrowing of the pelvic canal. This meant that the infant must be born with its nervous system relatively incomplete – a change made possible by the fact that an upright mother could hold and nurse it: in lower primates, where mother's hands were needed for locomotion, the baby must be born mature enough to hold on from birth. Once over the hurdle of early birth, with no pressure to complete brain-growth before it, the human baby, tended by its parents, could take time to develop both a relatively enormous brain, and the complex learning, itself time-consuming, which this made possible. Childhood lengthened to take this in, for big-brainedness was a sovereign evolutionary advantage. And from big-brainedness grew sociality and tradition. Another prerequisite of the process – that one should usually bear a single child at any one time – had been met earlier in primate history.

One is often tempted to interpret these changes chicken-and-egg-wise, and say that in human evolution A led to B, and B to C. This is a carry-over from the analogy – and it is false analogy – between evolutionary process viewed in retrospect and the effect of human planning; evolution does not plan and move in a straight line – it flows, and occupies vacant spaces. One breakthrough triggers others; these have subsidiary effects which expand the first. Processes can switch their function – reptiles evolved elaborate scales, probably in response to selection for purposes of temperature control; but the result enabled some of them to fly, for other selective forces modified them to give feathers. In looking back at human evolution we are not looking at a carefully executed plan but the end-product of a steady growth of potentialities, of expedients due to selection, to emergencies which in turn opened the way to new kinds of performance. Evolution occurs where equilibria are unstable – there are animals, like the brachiopod *Lingula*, which have stayed unchanged since the earliest fossil record. They represent the stable equilibria, but they do not evolve.

The family to which Man belongs is the *Hominidae*; literally 'sons of Man', but here sons only in the Arabic or Hebrew sense of 'human stock', for it includes cousins and ancestors rather than sons. The name covers all living and past men, as well as a race or races of early or ape-like men, the Australopithecines.

All other primates which can be traced back beyond the Pleistocene have recognizable lineages, but not the Man family. This family makes its appearance suddenly around the Lower Pleistocene – by the Middle Pleistocene, 300–350,000 years ago, hominids were living in Africa, in what is now the Middle East, in China, and in Java.

They seem to have sprung into the fossil record fully armed, but they must have come from somewhere; the chief candidate for their ancestor – in the direct or in a collateral line – is an ancient ape called *Proconsul*, who lived in the Early Miocene, some twenty millions of years ago. *Proconsul* stood in a stock which may since have produced the chimpanzees, gorillas and orang utangs, and probably also ourselves, the hominids, who differ from these anatomically in having bigger brains, smaller and flatter teeth, and the ability to walk upright. *Proconsul* may not be our direct ancestor – we may be descended from animals from which *Proconsul* too was descended – but at least he looks like a relative. The gibbon stock, with a family-pattern a little like ours, may have branched off about the same point, developing small-size and high-speed, Tarzan-style locomotion in trees, instead of turning to the ground and the development of two-footed walking.

All our libraries contain books on the origins of Man, illustrated with pictures of fossil skulls which are often arranged in some rough 'family tree'. These are drawn largely on a basis of chronology rather than any real evidence of inter-relationship – in other words, skull A is older than skull B, and skull C is younger still: arranged thus on the page, they at least show the order of the fossils in time, and since the subject of human ancestry is as difficult for the expert as for the layman, the reader is left to draw his own conclusions – with or without dotted lines – as to whether skull A was the daddy of them all. *This is something we cannot now know.* We know that in the lower Pleistocene (say half to one million years ago) there were Man-like apes, some of them tool-using; that by 500–550,000 years ago there were already 'ancient men' in Java and in China, who possessed tools, fire and probably developed speech. Later came men with unprepossessingly sloping skulls and 'foreheads villainous low' by comparison with the upright brow of modern Man, but equal to him in brain size and even, at one time, perhaps ahead of their truly modern-type contemporaries, both in techniques and in culture. These ugly but not unintelligent early men take their name from the valley where the first skull was found, and are called Neanderthalers. They were numerous and successful, but they disappeared, and *Homo sapiens*, who may have descended from them or from a common stock with them, and who probably interbred with them, became the dominant form.

This is the rough outline in time, but we can fill in very few of the details. Even if the unexplored areas give up their fossils it will be a matter of inference who descended from whom – it is even a matter of argument whether modern men all have an identical origin or not – whether, that is, modern men first appeared in one place, like a family of Adams, and then spread over the globe, or whether *sapiens* characters evolved in a widespread population of pre-*sapiens* men in several places, on several different occasions. These represent two distinct schools, the 'monophyletic' or one-family theory, and the 'polyphyletic' or several families theory. One form of the second is that the main ethnic groups – Caucasians, Mongolians, Australian Aborigines, Africans loosely ('Congoid' peoples) and Bushmen, Hottentots and Pygmies ('Capoid' peoples) – represent five separate emergences of modern *sapiens* Man, at five different times and places, which would account for the differences in appearance between them. (This theory has been loved and hated as a source of fuel for political racialism, but it provides none – the fact, if it is a fact, that they appeared at different times proves nothing whatever; anyone who quotes evolution to prove that seniority scores is on decidedly shaky ground, and in any case nobody knows who is senior – probably the African peoples, whom most of the would-be racialists are determined to denigrate.) Alternatively – and the majority of biologists concerned with this matter seem to prefer the alternative at present – these 'ethnic groups' are the products of evolution acting on *sapiens* as he spread into new environments by migration. At least they are manifestly all men and brothers, and arguments over their classification are largely academic. Indeed, Neanderthal Man, though he has been called a separate species, was probably just as much a man and a brother, eligible for membership on his intelligence and the fact that some skulls suggest intermediacy and interbreeding between Neanderthalers and *sapiens* men. The family history is already long. The earliest *Homo erectus* (Latin name of the immediate ancestor of 'our' kind of man – the Pekin and Java men) is believed to be about 700,000 years old. He appeared at a time when busy evolution was going on in a whole series of mammalian species, and may still have been holding out 100,000 years ago. The oldest candidates for full *sapiens* manhood appeared about 250,000 years ago, and the really modern men – like those of the five ethnic groups mentioned – may have been here not much more than 50,000 years ago. Judging from the extreme luck needed for us to find today a serviceable skull for identification, *sapiens* could have been much older if his numbers were small, and if his 'appearance' in our series of fossils represents not a new birth but a takeover bid by a species which had been biding its time to spread explosively. Pekin Man, the early man from China, had fire 360,000 years ago, and fire, it has been pointed out, is a focus for more than warmth and cooking – social communication, rites, story-telling and traditional skills go on round it. Life with *Sinanthropus* may have been less unfamiliar than the cast of his jaw and brow suggest – the Pygmy or Aborigine who scowls out of a still photograph does not look like 'one of us', but live with him, or even watch him on film, and the bond of common humanity is quite evident. Our dislike, as a species, of strangers and of the unfamiliar, which must have played a big part in our past evolution by keeping peoples apart, and is today behind much of the animosity between men who differ in appearance and custom, may bias us too much towards assuming that our ancestors were 'ape men' as depicted by cartoonists. After all, the Zulus used to regard all other ethnic groups as monkeys rather than men – Europeans and Africans included.

Students of primates are not now given to treating them – or other animals – as if they were quaint little men; this kind of anthropomorphism has greatly bedevilled our relations with animals, and has made us miss much which is intensely interesting in their behaviour, precisely at the point where it is *un*like ours. Yet in dealing with the higher primates the link is certainly there, and hardened primatologists[4] can write that in dealing with chimps they experienced 'the overwhelming conviction that one is dealing with an essentially human set of attitudes and motivations'; friendliness, anger, malice, desire for attention or thrills, curiosity and a form of social awareness like our own, which combines feeling with imagination and conceptual thought.

We find the unfamiliarity of other men harder to accept than that of animals, to whom we can feel effortlessly superior.

Something of the same kind may explain the divergence of opinion about the intelligence of our most immediate predecessor (if not ancestor – he may not be such) the Neanderthaler. Neanderthal is a small valley near Düsseldorf, named in honour of a local poet, the hymn-writer Neumann – who signed his hymns with the Greek translation of his German name, 'new man': Joachim Neander. It was a strange prevision. In 1856 a poorly-preserved skullcap with beetling brows and a few long bones were dug up in the hymnologist's valley. Since that time, similar skulls and bones in a better state have come to light from many other sites. Their owner was ape-like in the heavy brows, jutting jaws and barrel chest, but man-like in the brain capacity, erect in gait and a hunter who used fire – as his probable ancestors the ancient men of China (*Sinanthropus*) had done.

The main objection to regarding him as our direct ancestor is that there are older fossils more like modern Man than he was. Evidence from bones suggests that there were *sapiens* men 150,000 years ago, which makes them the Neanderthaler's contemporaries or predecessors. Later on, we find 'progressive' skulls, halfway between the two. Possibly in the vicissitudes of climate imposed by the Ice Ages the two kinds of man were separated geographically; during the Third interglacial Neanderthalers had a developed culture in Europe as cave-dwellers, fire-makers and skilled hunters, who made competent chipped stone tools. During the Fourth Ice Age, though not at its coldest point, Neanderthalers seem to have disappeared, to be replaced by new cave-dwellers who were modern-type men. Some have argued that *sapiens* took over Neanderthal techniques, others that he was 'primitive' by comparison with the lighter-browed, less toothy race and succumbed to better men. If so, he need not have been 'wiped out' by violence. Europeans are not now shooting down the Kalahari Bushman – he is as intelligent as they are, yet the contact of cultures will eventually, one must fear, prove fatal to his way of life.

A heavy-jawed Early Man whose remains have been found at Ishango, in Central Africa, and who lived about 8,500 years ago, made harpoons of beautiful design and left notches on a tool-handle which appear to be mathematical, and suggest the use of a decimal system and a knowledge of prime numbers.

Ishango Man was not a Neanderthaler; later cultures in the same region appear to have lost all the techniques which he invented, only recovering them centuries later.

All that we can write about the early evolution of Man is still largely guesswork, and about the stages of the process we know nothing. The changes described – or surmised – in the last chapter, the development of Oedipal drives, the lengthening of childhood and the like, fall far earlier in our history than the differentiation of modern men – at or about the time of *Proconsul*, one would surmise, when ape sexuality was giving way to family life, not among 'cave men' or primal hordes, as Freud surmised, and possibly about the point where gibbon ancestry branched off. All in all one would guess that such basic humanities, like the use of fire and tools, are older than we would have liked to think, and that we share large sections of our 'dream time' not only with unsophisticated modern men like the Aborigine, but with Pekin Man and even with his predecessors; for it was the interaction of these forces with growing intellectual powers, growing technical skill, and the social institutions formed from all these things which must have been the main selective influences in shaping the evolution of this unique new primate which could communicate, have institutions and customs, hold beliefs, and impart them to his children. Probably it is this interaction which is the most important thing for us to grasp about the process. The Freudian biologist who emphasises the sexual and unconscious effects on behaviour, the rationalist who sees the growth of humanness in terms of intelligent thought, the anthropologist who points to the importance of having a society, the Marxist who talks about techniques and the distribution of food and wealth, and the pure empiric who points out that to have tools you need hands on which you do not walk, are all right. 'English lacks any neat expression for this sort of situation, forcing us to speak of cause and effect as if they were separated, whereas in natural selection cause and effect are interrelated.'[5]

We have seen that tools may have originated before Man, and that Man discovered fire relatively soon after. Speech must have appeared about the same time, for Pekin Man hunted too effectively to have done so individually, and co-ordinated hunting parties require language. Throughout the period from 350,000 years ago until about 11,000 years ago, men were of two main occupations – food-gatherers, like the apes, or like some modern primitives, and hunters, like the Pygmies or the Eskimo. Most cultures probably did both. Hunting must have played a very large part in the shaping of early human institutions – it involves much transmission of lore, it may require leadership and organization, it both strains and develops the social sense of the group through the need to apportion the catch, and it seems to have provided a stimulus for art and for the kind of magical preparation and ritual which we see in modern hunting peoples, whose dances are half-magical, to secure success, and half-instructional, to secure good discipline in the field. Hunting also accentuates the division of labour; it is nearly always the male's task.

Lévi-Strauss has tried to reinterpret human marriage customs in terms of communication, treating woman as a 'message', exchanged between one tribe or family and another. As a repository of all this, she is certainly one of the most important pieces of social programming; even in repressive orders which insist that she 'keeps her mouth shut and her legs open', she programmes us verbally as children, while in our own society she is possibly the more talented intuitive communicator as against the male.

From this we might be led to wonder whether the next great human breakthrough – the biggest between the invention of fire and speech and the beginning of science – may not have been a feminine discovery. Until the evolution of agriculture, Man lived at the cultural pace laid down, or made possible, by ways acquired over 500,000 to 1,000,000 years – and differing little from the ways of *Sinanthropus*, save in complexity and polish. This is a staggering expanse of time when we consider that within a few thousand years of domesticating plants and animals, Man was living in cities, and within 10,000 years he was living in modern New York or London. This may not be a matter of cause and effect – indeed, from what we have said about the interaction of cause and effect in evolution, it was not. But it was yet another example of the breakthrough which accelerates the pace of an evolutionary process, and of the tendency of such processes to go faster and faster, each new development sending up the rate of change by one or more orders of magnitude. Up to that time Man had adapted himself to his environment – from that time he began increasingly to adapt the environment to himself.

The domestication of animals was probably accidental, because it can occur so easily. Human beings – especially children, who, among hunting peoples, can often catch cubs when they cannot kill adults – have a way of adopting even useless animals. Taken young, such cubs or lambs will grow around the village and breed spontaneously, either among themselves or with wild outsiders, but a settled site of residence makes this easier. (Nomads are often dependent on domestic herds, but to be this kind of nomad one must already possess herds – one could not acquire them accidentally while wandering.)

Plant domestication requires an even more settled residence, lasting more than a season. It involves a far bigger element of inspiration, though it might well originate by luck in the growth of seeds and tubers which had been scattered – what the Irish call 'volunteer' potatoes – helped by a peculiar attribute of the chief food grains. Wild wheat and barley have their seeds loosely fixed on the spike – as they must, to scatter effectively – but a few plants in such populations seem to have better-fixed seeds. Since these would be the easiest to carry home, Man may well have been unintentionally selecting the most desirable agricultural quality in wheat when he carried a bunch of it over his shoulder. Such selection in plants can work very fast – in the last century the sugar yield of beet was lifted in a few years to

49

an economic level by the simple and inspired dodge of planting only those roots which sank in brine. The fixed-seed wheat of today is wholly dependent on Man for the spread of its seeds, for it requires threshing, and will sprout uselessly in the spike if left.

Once again it looks as if domestication followed a settled way of life rather than that Man settled in order to farm (we should by now be familiar with these processes of two-way cause-effect) but that once settled he could and did farm, and became more settled. Dogs and goats appear to have been among the earliest animals to be domesticated; wheat, barley and possibly vetches were among the earliest plants.

The site of this revolution in human habits is usually placed in the so-called 'fertile crescent' of north Iraq and Iran (roughly from Aleppo on the Mediterranean to Mosul and Baghdad, and north to Lake Van), the traditional 'garden of Eden' where food-gathering gave way to hard work, where great floods, like those of Noah or Gilgamesh in the Babylonian epic, may have occurred, and where conditions for a move from cave to village were favourable all the year round. The chief ground for this view, apart form the tradition, is that this is about the only place where the staple plants and animals of early agriculture all occur wild, or did occur 10,000 years ago; and the result of archaeological digs at several sites in the area, which yield evidence of agriculture, bones and figurines of domestic animals, and sickle blades made of obsidian (volcanic glass) or flint, from older levels than are known elsewhere. It could well be that the revolution took place in more than one site, however (the rice-cultures, for instance, could have emerged separately). Evidence suggests that in Iran the village-farming culture moved slowly down from the hills into the Mesopotamian plain. Perhaps this was the epoch of flood legends – about 5,000 BC – not an ill fit with the old-time Biblical chronology which put Adam around 6,400 BC by totting up genealogies. By 4,000 BC there were sizeable cities, with the political conse-quences stemming from city formation; cities had kings – gods were no longer spirits but became kings of an extra-demanding complexion who presided, among other things, over fertility and seasons. Cattle had apparently resisted early domestication, but by now their curved horns were associated in many places with a cult of the Moon, who presides over tides, the fertility of women, and other cyclic events. Art was long since out of its infancy – beside the sensitive drawings of game which characterize cave-hunter and modern Bushman art it had long since produced figurines, including a remarkable range of little female figures, plump and pregnant with immense buttocks and breasts (often named from a famous example, the Venus of Willendorff) who seem to personify Enough to Eat, and pre-date the cave paintings by some 20,000 years. We cannot trace out all this, for the process of development, having once broken through the food-gathering barrier and got out of Eden into the modern world of techniques, moves at the pace of history, not of prehistory or of evolution – a new and unique pace in the story of change. Within 5,000 years, agriculture had spread and cities had begun; within another three or four thousand (by about 1,400 BC) metals were well in use, technology was far advanced, and a culture deeply interested in the seasons and the stars, for both practical and ritual reasons, was building vast stone calendar-temples at Stonehenge, Avebury, and later as far north as the Orkneys. These were not places where 'cave men' sacrificed each other, but where civilized men attempted to understand and perhaps control the objects in the sky overhead. There was one jump more to come, the jump into objective science, which took place only over the last five hundred years between the early Renaissance and ourselves, and has been full-grown for only a century.

There are areas on the map which we forget, because of the habit in schoolrooms of centering the map of the world on our home region. Thus an Englishman readily forgets what lies between, say, New York and Chicago, or Paris and Prague, through having spent his youth looking at a map with England in its centre and the rest of the world receding on either side.

We do the same looking back in time – in thinking how long Man has been there, we forget the silent periods separating tools from speech, speech and hunting from agriculture, and agriculture from civilization. The planet we live on appears by most reckonings to have been in existence for about 5,000 million years. From 'the beginning' so dated to the emergence of life was, say, 2,750 million years. From the origin of life to the ape-ancestor *Proconsul* was about 2,230 million years: from *Proconsul* to the use of tools, say nineteen million. From tools to the present day has taken under one million, with fire and speech at about 0·4 million, agriculture at 0·01 million (10,000 years) and science at a mere five hundred or less – 0·0005 million years. Thus if our whole history from the start of our cosmic process were plotted on a line five kilometres long, the distance between the start of agriculture and the present day would be one centimetre, and the duration of science about a half a millimetre. That is the measure of the change in rate.

Perhaps the oddest thing about it is that change should have taken place so rarely. Man is not obliged by his nature to evolve at the social level, any more than the old fossil *Lingula* at the biological. There are peoples today making stone implements exactly like those of neolithic Man, and food-gatherers living much as Pekin Man must have done. The great breakthroughs are characteristically local and once-for-all; it was the agriculturalists of the Eastern Mediterranean who broke through to cities and to further civilization which spread East and West; it was the city technological society of Europe that broke through to science – equally cultured societies in the past, and in China, India and South America had failed to make this precise breakthrough. We may speculate why – it would be more profitable, if we would forsee the next move of comparable importance, to do so purposively. If we could do this, and change our society to make it more likely to achieve such a breakthrough, evolution would finally have escalated into purpose; through science we have gone some way in this direction, but the social sector remains for us to control.

Chapter 4

Human Variability

SOME animals show remarkably little variation. All the crows or seagulls of one species that one has ever seen are monotonously alike. By contrast, some other species are extremely variable. This variation may be of two kinds – animals which show wide variation in one place are said to be polymorphic; those which vary widely from place to place, or in different populations or colonies, are said to be polytypic. Man is both.

A big dog show, or the population of San Francisco, illustrate polymorphism. One finds dogs ranging from the wolfhound, as big as a small pony, to the chihuahua, as big as a large rat, and of all degrees of height, squatness, woolliness, snub-nosedness, and temperament. This dog-show polymorphism is in truth artificial, for it has been created by selective breeding of a lot of strains which are now kept artificially apart by Man, as subspecies in nature are kept apart by geography. Turned loose to breed, the dog population would be polymorphic for a long time, but would in the end tend to the 'average' dog, or to several subspecies.

Part of the polymorphism of the humans in San Francisco is due to a similar effect – their ancestors came from geographically separate places, looked different from each other, and have to some extent stayed separate through Japanese marrying Japanese and Swedes marrying Swedes, even within the city population. The very big range of skin and hair colour, facial appearance and build between the different ethnic groups is one part of the diversity we see in a city street. San Franciscan man is polytypic – Swedes may on the average be taller than Japanese; but there are tall and short Swedes, tall and short Japanese. Each of these national groups is itself a mixture of older local groups. But even within a small inbreeding tribe, who tend to look alike, Man is much more polymorphic than many other animals, and this polymorphism is not simply the product of the fact that we look more sharply at our own kind and therefore detect differences. We are sharply divided as a species by measurable characters which we cannot see – blood group, ability to taste particular chemicals, amount of acid in our stomachs. If we could see all these differences, then the most homogeneous-looking tribe or family would be seen to be as diverse as the population of any big immigrant city.

The first and most striking interhuman differences are the polytypic differences – those between ethnic groups. These are accentuated in our minds at the present time because of their political and social associations, but they are not biologically the most important, and some other cultures would have made much less of them. We have mentioned the dispute over the origin of these so-called 'races' of Man – whether they represent separate emergences of *sapiens* Man from a world-wide ancestor, or variation produced in a single population as it spread to new habitats. Their evolutionary importance might be clearer if we did not give so much weight to face shape and skin colour – two factors of recognition between people which are psychologically important to us – and gave more to body build in relation to height.

Why the different peoples acquired their present physical attributes is far from clear. Some were presumably adaptive; it can hardly be an accident that nearly all the peoples native to the tropical belt are dark-skinned even when ethnically unrelated, like the Zulus, the Bengalis and the Pygmies. The exception is for the tropical American Indians: one dark race (the Tasmanians) lived in a temperate climate before their extinction in the nineteenth century. One might ideally have expected some race exposed to intense sunlight – perhaps at high altitudes, rather than in the tropics – to become silver all over like a barrage balloon, using a silvery reflecting layer such as one finds in fish, for a black object takes up solar heat rapidly. This does not seem to have been in the evolutionary repertoire, however. The ancestors of the tropical peoples seem to have evolved a means of anticipating the built-in response of a pale skin to ultraviolet light by the selection of inherently dark individuals (camouflage in hunting has been suggested as another, perhaps incidental, advantage of darkness) while the high efficiency of the human sweating mechanism was more than enough to compensate for any black-body heating-effect.

Skin colour attracts our notice for psychological reasons. It is one of the 'prestige' attributes which are subject to social selection in many societies, partly because it suggests hard work and consequently poverty; thus higher-caste Hindus are said to be lighter-skinned than lower. This may reflect an ethnic element in the original castes, but since in various periods and places the chief breach of caste intermarriage has been through a higher-caste male marrying a lower-caste female, there has also been a prestige-element in the selection of paler spouses. By contrast nearly all races dislike the look of true albino humans (with white hair and pink eyes) though they have bred albino animals for their looks.

Pigmentation is not simply heritable, and several genes appear to be involved; in any homogeneous population it is continuously distributed. The theory that the possession of a remote Negro ancestor will produce a sporadic dark-skinned child, or a white ancestor a sporadic white-skinned child, at several generations remove, is not supported by experience (facial traits would be more likely to behave in this way). The average colour of the children of a marriage between Negro and European will be roughly midway between the parental tints. The unsavoury expertise which has grown up in race-minded communities for the detection of those who should be permitted to 'pass' or not permitted to 'pass' is more related to the medieval search for witches than to biology. As well as ethnic differences, which represent polytypy, there are big differences within a 'white' population in the amount of pigment formed in response to sunlight – some bronze, some burn, and some freckle. It is to cover this polymorphism that cosmetics have been developed to simulate the effects of sun. It would interest a Martian to hear a 'white' lady in one of the more race-minded communities explain why she would object to a dark-skinned mate or ancestor, but is pathetically proud of her laboriously won tan.

We may suppose that skin-colour is or was adaptive, but the fact remains that, save for those white individuals who burn without tanning, no race seems to be at a marked advantage or disadvantage today by reason of colour in their encounters with heat or sunlight. The only exception is in the slightly higher resistance to skin cancer seen in dark-skinned peoples over the parts of the body exposed to sun. Apart from this and the fact that they do not suffer from sunburn, Negroes do not have any very great advantage in standing up to heat compared with *adapted* white men. A more important adaptation to hot conditions is probably the long thin stature of some African peoples, and the small light build of other hot-climate dwellers, which give the maximum cooling surface for a given body weight. Snub noses and curly hair, though not universal in the tropics, are commoner there. One can only speculate about their origins. It might be more instructive to ask why European noses are thin and pointed, since the snub pattern may be the older, persisting where a special air-warming or air-moistening mechanism was no advantage. Hair length is more obviously a protection against cold, as is copious beard growth (the one really hairy race, the Ainu, live in a not over-cold part of Japan, however – the utility of 'jobbing backwards' in evolution soon runs out, and one is left with blind guesswork).

Some more solid guesses have been directed at the Mongolian

group of characters. Mongols spread from an area where winters are exceptionally severe, and have been treated as 'cold adapted' peoples; their descendants today include Eskimos, Red Indians and the hot-climate peoples of some parts of south-eastern Asia, but the typical Mongol was a cold-climate man, and his chunky build, his fat metabolism, his flat, frost-proof face, and his epicanthic fold, which gives him his slant-eyed appearance, and has been said to protect the tear-gland from excessive wind-exposure, may all be adaptations to survival under the chilly conditions of the Mongolian plain. They are certainly most marked in this area and among the Eskimo, and most diluted in the less exacting parts of Mongolian man's range. No other peoples have managed to survive in the really chilly parts of the earth until the advent of modern technology. Here there does appear to be evidence of better performance under cold conditions than in adapted men of other races; Alaskan Indians, for example, seemed to respond to cold by burning more oxygen and calories in sleep, so that they could remain asleep at temperatures which woke Europeans. The same applies to the Fuegian Indians of Patagonia, who dive, canoe and swim naked in icy water – their basal metabolism was 160 per cent higher than in Europeans of similar stature. The unrelated Australian Aborigines have a different kind of cold adaptation; their skin temperature falls, but circulation through the extremities is reduced during sleep and their bodies remain internally warm, using the outer layers of skin and muscle as an overcoat, while naked Europeans lose heat through the skin and are woken by shivering.

Peoples, accordingly, differ – certainly in appearance, possibly in adaptation. For reasons at which we have hinted already, one cannot touch this subject without raising anxiety. That anxiety springs from two main sources. The first is a deep-rooted cultural fear of strangers – they may be more knowing, more powerful, more successful sexually than we; worst of all – if we are a primitive people – they may have magical abilities they can direct against us.

The second source of anxiety is historical. History has put some ethnic groups on top. In Singapore the Chinese are indeed richer than the Malays. The white European (including the American) has indeed governed the world for a hundred years, through the possession of technology and the knowledge that

> 'whatever happens we have got
> the Gatling Gun, and they have not.'

If one is not a white European, the idea sticks – not unnaturally. It is not very much over a century since the European ethnic group was shipping Africans to the plantations – and so on. Also, we have lived through a bad twenty years, which were all the worse for coming at a time when men of goodwill were gaining confidence in the stability of a new moral adaptation for the race as a whole. In anti-Semitism, anti-Negroism, anti-White-ism and anti-humanism generally the two sources of anxiety fuse. We *are* still potentially a primitive people. If our 'dream-time' contains, as it does, the sleeping material of all human sociality, it also contains deadly and explosive material which, given certain social conditions, can erupt into terrifying disorder.

For these reasons every decent person now finds the topic of race embarrassing – it excites anxiety, guilt and foreboding about the future and our own precarious civilization of mind – and every decent biologist tries to avoid waking any more tigers by some unguarded remark. Suggest that Man might have evolved on more than one occasion, and one may set some idiot declaring that the Chinese or the Aborigines are submen. Investigate differences of adaptation, and one may find oneself quoted to prove the natural right of alphas to govern betas. We have said much that was optimistic and inspiring about the human breakthrough into sociality, but the topic of human differences brings us up against the other side of the medal, the persistence in Man of irrationalities which mean that we are playing double or quits for the future. We have always been doing so, and in spite of massacres and tyrants we have done so successfully. Our eighteenth-century ancestor looking round him would have seen more injustice and brutality in daily life than we can tolerate today without guilt. He would have seen slavery while we only see gross exploitation in some places. He would unashamedly have considered himself the most progressive example of the species. He would have forseen growing humanism and sense of guilt over our residual hatreds, however, and he would have had the conviction that Man was getting better. *His* predecessors would not have been so sure – they would have attributed much of the evil in human treatment of Man to a Devil, who was the source of such unbiddable evils, and the enemy of the God who was Love. (Unfamiliar peoples were heathens and probably his devotees.) By the start of the scientific revolution, the Devil was dying out of our minds, and compelling us to realize that devilry originates in the same place as progress, inside ourselves. Compared with our eighteenth-century great-great-grandfather we are more squeamish, more responsible, and more concerned about Man. But Freud and Darwin and the atomic bomb have made us less confident.

We shall have more to say about this later. Part of our anxiety over race springs from the fact that we have knowledge now about our motives and the depth of our potential irrationality – which gives us the possibility of controlling them, but also, together with recent history, shows us how precarious the balance is. We are also the first generation which could destroy life on earth if it fails to behave with moderation.

In fact, biology and anthropology are about the best antidotes to human antagonisms at the irrational level that could be devised. A generation ago, for most of the Western world and for many peoples outside it, all strangers were 'savages', with uncouth habits and warlike intentions – just as to the European townsman all animals were potentially savage and liable to attack on sight. The feathered dancer celebrating something we did not understand, the Neanderthaler with his bony scowl in the book about evolution, and the gorilla paterfamilias thumping on his chest were all unpleasant strangers who meant us no good. There were indeed aggressive peoples (not least the European adventurers) and some territory-keeping animals on whose stamping-ground it is foolish to intrude. But the savage and the wild beast were to a large extent a mirror in which we saw reflected aspects of our own nature which we could not face directly. Victorian Englishmen in India would not look at the effigy of the Goddess Kali, the Destroyer and Drinker of Blood – only barbarians would have such a goddess. Within a few years, come the Mutiny, they were behaving to innocent and guilty alike with a fury which demonstrated her reality. The Hindus, who made her the counterpart of Creation and of Change, knew better.

There is no better antidote to the fear of wild beasts than knowing animals, and no better antidote to the fear of other men than knowing other men. And indeed the study of races and their differences need alarm nobody, because the most salient fact to come out of the study of human diversity is precisely the fact of human identity. It emphasizes the difference between real ethnic diversity, which is an interesting phenomenon, increasing the range of human potentialities, so that many an Olympic high-jumper draws his physique from a Zulu and his stature from an enormously long-legged Watutsi. At the same time it effectively knocks on the head the kind of racialism preached by the Nazis – the unfortunate Jews against whom their malice was directed were not even an ethnic group, but a religious community which had some genetic identity through the custom of intermarriage.

It is not theoretically impossible that ethnic groups differ in aptitudes other than cold adaptation or resistance to sunburn – it might possibly be that intuitive perception of cube roots is genetic, and that it is commoner in Chinese than in Pygmies. But the prestige-conferring abilities, which are those which make us anxious about race, in case we ourselves prove superior or inferior, are practically uninvestigable. In the event, the European peoples have made the technical breakthrough – our brash ancestors thought the proof of the pudding was in the eating, and this made them superior, at least by the test of performance. Granting the performance, this is pretty questionable. Nobody could seriously suggest that European thinkers are more – or less – ingenious than the Chinese sage or the Indian philosopher. If any genetic trait contributed to the ascendancy of one over the other it was far more probably some irrelevant character now buried under a vast pile of subsequent history. Most likely of all it was simply cultural accident – perhaps it was a maladaptation, like the increased liability to neurotic 'drives' which made us hell-bent on all our activities. Such speculation is now pointless.

It looks theoretically unlikely that races as we see them today differ much in intelligence, if by that we mean the basic brain quality which makes for learning and faster adaptation, and if they did one could not prove it. An Aborigine would score badly on our tests, but these tests are made for members of a reading and writing culture. We would score very low upon his tests of tracking, desert knowledge and resourcefulness. Underprivileged peoples score badly by tests devised for privileged peoples. There are not fewer Negro DSc's than there are European DSc's because Negroes are genetically unable to learn calculus – other reasons for the disparity suggest themselves to any unbiassed observer. In other words, just as in sexual behaviour the built-in patterns of other primates are overridden in Man by cultural and personal patterns, so any genetic differences between the aptitudes of ethnic groups are swamped by cultural factors of far greater significance; it seems pointless to look for them at the moment. If and when we do identify them they may not comfort those of any race who think themselves inherently superior to their fellows. The Aborigine or the Pygmy may have the aptitudes, on a basis of equal competition, which make him the author of the next intellectual and social breakthrough. Adversity may make some of us shine – men who lose their hands learn to sew with their toes, which they would never otherwise have done. The high proportion of great musicians, artists and scientists who are Jews may owe their success to genetics – they probably also owe it to being members of a community which was picked on and excluded from many pursuits, so that it clung to a tradition of scholarship, hard work and determination to be treated as equals.

It is obvious that such social factors can feed back into genetics. A caste who could only be blacksmiths must be muscular or starve – and indeed the Indian castes who are tied strictly to occupation, and even perhaps the social classes of the old, rigid European societies, have come to differ in appearance. But these are among the less important types of polymorphism in Man, and a few generations of social interbreeding would soon abolish them. We can see some of the main types of polymorphism within a community of one main ethnic group in any street full of white Americans, of Chinese, or of Negroes. Polymorphic characters are of two kinds, all or none and graded. Graded characters include such things as stature, intelligence and size of hat worn. All or none characters may be obvious – an albino, who has white hair and pink eyes, is one such. Blood groups are another. One can have in one's red blood cells antigen A, antigen B, both, or neither. There are thus four kinds of people classified in this way, and there are no intergrades. Since there are many other blood-group systems now known, and each is inherited separately, hardly any two individuals have an identical constitution in this respect except monozygotic twins.

One important diversity of the either/or kind, present in all human communities, is between men and women. This is hardly a polymorphism, but it has been the focus of a crop of irrationalities as bitter as those over race – with the difference that here there is a demonstrable biological difference, and it would not be unreasonable to expect that of the temperamental differences between the sexes which we see, or profess to see, in our own or other societies some are learned and some are built-in. Sex roles – mannishness or womanishness in the terms laid down by a given culture – and even sexual behaviour are almost wholly learned, for a child brought up in the 'wrong' sex will conform to our expectation for the sex in which it was reared. The nature of the Oedipal fears and their representation in the two sexes may basically affect other attitudes; beside these, biological differences tend to be obscured, though they are probably present. Once more, the built-in element in a human response is subordinated so fully to learning that it becomes almost impossible to dissect out, save in contexts as factual as the greater resistance of women to exposure, cold and the like. If in a given society there are fewer women mathematicians or members of the Supreme Court than there are males in these occupations, the reason is probably little more biological than the reason for the shortage of Eskimos in these occupations.

Beside such yes/no differences as sex and blood group, there are a number of characters which one could most properly term sporadic, and which it is difficult to grade with certainty as all-or-none or continuously distributed. One such is bone number – clearly one either has a particular bone or one has not; on the other hand five per cent of us have six lumbar vertebrae, ninety-two per cent have five, and three per cent have four. A few of us have extra bones or sutures in our skulls. Some of us have four instead of three thumb bones. This is a disadvantage from the functional point of view, and in being so it brings us to the most important aspect of human variation, at least so far as our attitudes towards it in science and medicine are concerned. That attitude – or rather the need to revise it – arises from our use in common speech of the word 'normal'.

Men normally walk upright without falling, i.e. if one falls he has tripped, or there is something the matter with him, and birds normally fly straight. However there is a variety of pigeon, the tumbler, which seldom flies straight, but keeps repeating the aerobatic dodge by which pigeons avoid a hawk attack, and pigeons of this breed normally tumble. We normally have five lumbar vertebrae. If we have more or less, there is no reason why we should notice the fact; but suppose the four-vertebrae condition led to violent backache – in that case the surgeon might well advise us to have the vertebrae fused, to restore normality of function. Having an extra thumb-joint is a statistical abnormality – it is also a nuisance. So is albinism, for it leads to sore eyes and severe sunburn. These conditions figure in books on medical genetics as diseases. Being of blood group A is not a disease; about forty-five per cent of Englishmen are of that group. But it has been found that members of this blood group have a higher incidence of cancer of the stomach than other groups. Is it an abnormality? I have virtually no stomach acid, in common with at least ten per cent of my fellows, and the lack of it predisposes me to certain kinds of anaemia. But if I had stomach acid, I would be more likely than I now am to have a gastric ulcer. Are both acid-production and non-acid-production abnormalities?

This whole matter is our own fault linguistically. We use the word normal to mean: (1) common or commonest – black hair is normal in Negroes, Chinese and Bengalis, but in a few people of these races it is red; five-vertebrae lumbar spines are normal to Man as a whole, but a few have more or less. In other words, these are the commonest states to find, though there are also exceptions. It may also mean: (2) working as we would wish our body to work, without pain, disability or shortening of life – in other words, a value-judgment. In this sense it means 'optimal', or, failing that, the best we can do. Mathematicians complicate the matter further by using normal (3) to describe a particular statistical distribution, that which characterizes a continuously distributed variable like height, which, in Man, is said to be normally distributed: (this one is a technical outsider, but since it gets into our discussion of human variation we have to mention it).

It takes no deep penetration to see that (1) and (2) above may well clash (in some societies it is normal to suffer from an abnormality like neurosis or hookworm) or that normal, like natural, can be used as an emotive missile ('he's abnormal'), especially where it applies to variation in behaviour or psychology. Here, for the reasons we have already given concerning cultural and learned influences on behaviour, reference to the normal and the natural, without further particularization, are even more pointless. In some cultures it has been grossly abnormal to bury a dead relative rather than eat him decently: in our culture such a funeral would be evidence of grave mental disorder. Homosexual attraction to little boys is in our culture both an abnormality and – if acted upon – a crime: in classical Greece it was a fashionable affectation. And so on.

The importance of normality as a word-obstacle is perhaps greatest in medicine, where our forbears attempted as often as not to restore what they conceived to be the normal state. Modern work on the variation of Man puts such a concept out of court, except in very simple contexts. The villagers who attempted to wash a Negro white were unaware that Man was polytypic; we have only just realized that he is polymorphic as well.

More accurately, we have always realized it, but our knowledge of that polymorphism is only just coming to a useful point. The ancient physicians of Europe divided men by temperaments – they were choleric, melancholic, bilious, hypochondriac, according to the relative predominance of the Four Elements, earth, air, fire and water. Hindu medicine adopted similar classifications by type and by temperament – each temperament had its peculiar diseases and its psychological attributes – but some of them, the writers of sexual treatises in particular, were stimulated by the great ethnic variety of India to start classifying human types by shape. The object of this exercise was to match man and woman for the most satisfactory sexual result; initially it was based simply on physical size. In the ancient *Kāmasūtra* of Vatsyayana (500 BC), men are hares, oxen or stallions, and women gazelles, mares or elephantesses, according to build and genital dimensions (in real life, as opposed to tradition, the two do not coincide to any useful extent). By the Middle Ages we find a new classification, especially of women, who are now 'lotus ladies', 'picture ladies', 'seashell ladies' and 'elephant ladies', each with their special attractions (a modern French

65

writer classifies them, with much the same amatory intentions, as vase-shaped, barrel-shaped, big 'uns and miniatures). Such classifications were not biological accounts of variation, but more like the Kennel Club's specifications – the chosen spouse was a good specimen insofar as she conformed to one of the breeds. Yet we can see in this ancient idea the germ of another far more important concept, that human beings differ within a population at least as much as do the so-called races, that such differences could be quantified, and that they are important because other physical and psychological attributes correlate with them. The old physicians noted particular individuals who, from their look, could be regarded as candidates for a particular illness – Hippocrates (460–375 BC) described the 'apoplectic' and the 'phthisic' types, the fat florid man who might have a stroke, and the thin cadaverous man who was a candidate for consumption, but it was not until the nineteenth century that the German psychiatrist Kretschmer, in trying to correlate shape with behaviour and temperament, devised the name 'constitutional type' for each of the main kinds of body configuration. We now call such classificatory groups *somatotypes* (Greek, soma, body).

Kretschmer's constitutional types were three, the 'pyknic' (beaten-down and well-rounded) the 'athletic' (muscular and well-built) and the 'asthenic', (long, thin and round-shouldered) each of whom he considered more prone than his fellows to particular mental illness – the pyknic to cyclical fits of depression, and the asthenic to schizophrenia. There was behind this classification the idea that these 'pure types' represented original strains of men, the intermediates (most of us) being, as it were, mongrels – a notion which Prof Theodosius Dobzhansky says is 'like supposing that all human dwellings came by mixing the Empire State Building with an Eskimo igloo'.

A better way of classifying shape depends on the realization that its three main components – bone, fat and muscle – vary quite independently. Attempts have also been made to score every individual on three scales representing visceral (endomorphy) muscular-skeletal (mesomorphy) and skin and nervous system development (ectomorphy): this system doe s not reflec the independent variation of bone, muscle and fat, but it is the one most often quoted. No system of scoring is yet satisfactory. But the idea is there, and a start has been made upon the classification of people by shape, a necessary beginning to the task of finding what physical attributes commonly correlate with one another. Crude associations – between the florid man and having a stroke, or the thin flat chest and having tuberculosis – we already know. Sheldon, who devised the system cited here, has found certain somatotypes 'characteristic of delinquent boys, generals, business leaders, people showing Christian renunciation, people who do not attend college, etcetera' (Dobzhansky) – about the validity of which one may argue. Yet the fact remains that from now on normality= prevalence has to be broken down. There is not one genotypic (constitutional) normal but many, intergrading in some cases, all-or-none in another, and our question becomes not 'Is this normal?' but 'What manner of man is this?' The old rabbis who, on seeing a dwarf or a hunchback, would praise God who made his creatures of diverse forms, apparently had the right idea biologically speaking. As with all polymorphism, selection will often modify it, to favour long thin Dinkas or Watutsi in hot dry places, and barrel-shaped 'endomorphic' Eskimos in cold places, but by interbreeding and in neutral or man-made environments the whole potential variety will blossom, and there are few somatotypes, whatever their drawbacks, which could not have corresponding compensations.

Another and a socially important variation in Man, associated in part with body shape, concerns the age and pattern of puberty. This is both genetically and environmentally influenced, and the pattern of events – the time of occurrence of the various phenomena of approaching maturity and the order in which they occur – differ in children of different build. The exact nature of individual variation in age and pattern of puberty is under special study today for two reasons; first because in privileged countries the age of puberty as a whole has shifted steadily over the last few years to earlier ages, for reasons which are not adequately understood, and secondly because the spurt of growth which precedes puberty is attended by a spurt in the development of the adult intelligence, so that early developers are brighter for their age than late developers.

There is no one index of puberty. In girls we can score the development of the breasts and the adult female distribution of body fat, and the age of onset of menstruation; in boys, the change of voice, the growth of the genital organs and the appearance of sexual activity; in both sexes we can score the adolescent growth spurt, appearance of body hair and the age of attaining full stature. The order in which these occur differs slightly in different individuals – thus some boys fatten like girls, then develop muscle, while others become long and thin and only attain their final strength in relation to size at a later stage. The age of onset of each character has probably a normal distribution, and the whole process extends over a number of years.

The clock mechanism which initiates puberty is probably situated in the hypothalamus of the brain, the region which exercises control over many hormone processes through the nearby pituitary gland. Age of puberty runs in families – some families are known to be consistently late and others early by comparison with their neighbours. The extreme example of this kind is found in the rare group of cases (usually in little girls) where full-scale puberty takes place at five or six or even earlier, producing a miniature adult with the figure and body-hair distribution of a normal sixteen-year-old, who menstruates and can even conceive and bear a child. A girl of five is said to have done so. After puberty in humans the ends of the long bones become joined to the shaft, so that further growth is impossible. In constitutional precocious puberty this happens so early that full stature is never attained, and the subject is rarely much over four foot six inches tall. These cases are not due to disease but to genetics, and it is important to recognize families in which they occur, so as to avoid needless operations – for precocious puberty can also be triggered by tumours of the brain and abnormalities of the hormones. The children are often bright for their age, but if they are treated as children their psychosexual development and, oddly enough, the age at which the teeth erupt, follow the normal age scale. Unless hurried on by adults, such a child is not usually socially precocious – she is 'an unselfconscious child, exuberantly living a child's life, through its various phases of learning and maturation, in an adult's body'.[6] Such cases represent the shortening of the plateau of delayed growth and development which characterizes Man and the higher primates – the extreme cases have a growth curve like a lower mammal, with no lag phase at all. Less extreme cases are merely early: puberty may be well advanced by nine or ten. The Abbé Brantôme, sixteenth-century author of the *Lives of Gay Ladies*, a noted work devoted to gossip and scandal, peppered with some extremely amusing anecdotes, wrote:

Some girls do not wait the normal age of maturity, which falls about twelve or thirteen years, before seeking out love, but turn thither much sooner. Thus it happened not twelve years since in Paris that a pastrycook's daughter fell pregnant at the age of nine, and she being therewith very sick her father took her water to the Physician; who told him, that she had no other malady but pregnancy. 'What,' said the father, 'My daughter, Sir, is only nine years old!' Who so astounded as the Physician!

Brantôme apologizes for telling this story – not because it struck him as improper, but because it concerned the daughter, not of a lord, but a mere artisan. Other little girls are correspondingly late, with no evidence of abnormality.

Several other factors are known to influence the age of puberty in girls. Race may play some part – Japanese-Americans appear to be slightly later than Americans of European origin in comparable social circumstances. The old belief that puberty is signally early in hot countries or among dark-skinned races is quite false, however – it is if anything later at the equator than in Europe today. One quite unexplained correlate of rather early puberty in girls is blindness; in the blind, the menarche is earlier than normal, and earliest where there is no light-perception at all.[7] Economic prosperity favours earlier development all round, the mean age of menarche being lowest in the highest income group. Of the body builds, it has been said that the pyknic (stocky) group are earliest, the tall and thin next, and the 'average' build latest of all, but this needs confirmation.

Over the last century, in all the countries of Europe for which we have figures, children appear to have been reaching puberty earlier and earlier. This has nothing to do with the supposed social or sexual precocity of behaviour in young people; adults of every generation have tended to criticize their juniors as being undesirably precocious, but change of this sort, if real, is presumably a matter of social custom. The change in age of puberty, however, refers to objective measurements such as the age of first menstruation, or the age at which growth ceases. If we take the first of these as a marker, over the century from 1850 to 1950 the average age of menarche of girls in Scandinavia, England and America has been getting quite steadily earlier at the rate of one-third to one-half a year per decade, and appears to be still falling. Over the century, therefore, it has come down from about seventeen to about thirteen years. Puberty in boys is less easy to date, but it too appears to have advanced in the same way.

Some biologists have doubted the reality of this shift, but most accept it, and find it of great interest, for though we can guess at its causes we cannot be certain of them. It is only one of several changes which have been taking place in the pattern of child growth in privileged countries. As early as five years old, the children born in the 1930's were already much bigger than those born in the 1900's, and the children born in the 1950's were bigger still. Judging by relative size, Swedish children, for whom we have some of the best figures, had gained nearly a year and a half between the age-group born in 1938–9 and that born in the 1880's. Like the fall in age of menarche, the increase in height and weight has gone on quite steadily and shows no sign of stopping yet. Growth is not only being accelerated, but the final heights and weights reached are greater as well as being attained earlier. Some fifty years ago, maximum stature was not being reached on the average until about the age of twenty-nine. In the prosperous classes in Western Europe and America it is now reached about nineteen in boys and sixteen to seventeen in girls, and the final average height has gone up by about five centimetres.

There are phenomena about which a good many inferences have been drawn, some sound and some not. The first thing we would naturally like to know is what causes the gain. The most obvious thing which is likely to have done so is better nutrition, and, in general, better social conditions. This probably does explain most of it, but it has not satisfied everybody. Some biologists have wondered if part of the effect may be genetic. They put it down to the way in which the industrial revolution scattered populations which had formerly lived in villages and had become gradually inbred, and attribute it to 'the invention of the bicycle', the idea being that intermarriage produced a form of what is known as 'hybrid vigour'. This is not an explanation on which we should be wise to bet very heavily, and the one or two attempts to confirm it genetically have been negative. Another theory has been climatic: we know that overheating delays the growth of laboratory rats, and it has been suggested that our children may grow considerably faster now we no longer overclothe them, first in the mistaken interests of warmth and later in the equally mistaken interests of decency.

So far as the actual age of puberty is concerned there is good evidence that what has happened is not a radical change in our biology, but the restoration of a more normal developmental timing which something at the beginning of the nineteenth century had greatly slowed down. The average age of puberty in girls is now between twelve and a half and thirteen. In Roman Law it appears to have been about the same. The Abbé Brantôme, who was writing in the sixteenth century, puts the ordinary age of puberty at twelve to thirteen years. Johann Theodore Schenk wrote in 1664 (in his *Treatise on Excessive Menstrual Flow*):

Nature acting with unfailing Law and Regularity ordains for the onset of the courses the fourteenth year of age, at which time most women become subject thereto, and to the changes attending it. Puberty follows, the breasts swell, and some feel no little venereal desire. Seeing these signs the maiden rejoices, bespeaks herself a husband, glories in her twin breasts, loves to be loved, to couple, to mate.

Martinus Schurig, who invented the word 'gynaecology', quotes in 1729 the various opinions of ancient writers, giving a mean of twelve in girls and fourteen in boys – he thinks twelve is early for Europe and inclines to fourteen in both sexes. He goes on to say that blushing is a sure test of virginity – *dum erubescit, salva res est*. (If she still blushes, it's all right.)

Early marriage in old records, or in the Orient, is no evidence of age of puberty, since children were sometimes married while still immature, for dynastic reasons. In one of the oldest statistical studies, Dr J. M. Waddy of the Birmingham Lying-In Hospital (England) gave the following ages of menarche in factory-girls, published in 1846:

Age	Cases	Age	Cases
9	1	15	115
10	2	16	105
11	15	17	67
12	46	18	43
13	87	19	10
14	130	20	2

This suggests later onset than today, but not so much as some other series of figures. In France, the mean age of menarche apparently fell from over fifteen to about fourteen and a half over the years 1860–80, rose again up to 1890, and has fallen steadily ever since.

It appears therefore (as already stated) that much of the

apparent fall in the age of puberty is a return to normal after the operation of some factor which retarded puberty during the early half of the last century. While opinions differ over the cause and extent of the change, it now seems clear that we are seeing the full range of genetic variation in rate of development – in other words, under present conditions, potentially fast developers are able to do something approaching their best. In consequence we are becoming aware of the very large scatter in such rates among normal children. At fourteen years of age, some boys are palpably young men while others are still children. This variation is very interesting in its relation to body build, but it is important because of its bearing on our educational system, which is geared to age, not to rate of development. This is particularly important because of the link between intellectual and physical development. Recent studies which attempted to find out whether the level of average intelligence is changing have run into trouble because of the faster development of the population. At the same time, in England especially, where a child's school career may depend on success in tests taken at the age of eleven, the early developer, who can muster a mental age of thirteen at a real age of eleven, is at a huge advantage. He may not be able to keep up his lead, and his final adult performance may be poorer than that of another child who develops more slowly, but in a world of tests and examinations he has the edge over the rest of the class. Socially, too, the fact of being late or early could be expected to exert an influence – just as stature appears to do – upon self-confidence, dominance and social success. At the moment these are matters of which our schools take little cognisance, and the public is unaware of the advantages conferred by being early. This may be as well, for parents in a highly-competitive educational system who already pay to have their children coached through intelligence tests are not above trying to accelerate their development by heavy feeding, or even hormones.

The consequence of growing fast and growing early are not known, but they do not seem – as some biologists have feared –

to include shortening of life; in fact, as puberty has got earlier the menopause, another individually variable character, has got later; life has also got longer, though this reflects a reduction in preventable early deaths from disease, childbirth and so on.

In this respect, as in others, then, variation supersedes 'normality' as a concept. It also supersedes another and more dangerous matter, 'equality'. What we have said as between races applies here between men, for we do not confine injustice, suspicion or oppression to strangers, and dominance-behaviour in the less sociable human societies, including our own commercial-urban culture over its history, can be as fierce as among baboons and far less restrained. If we use the same confused terminology over human attainments that we used over what is normal, we may find ourselves endorsing a humane falsehood for fear of committing an indecency against Man – all men are not equal, if by this we mean that their powers or weaknesses in any field at all are identical. No two individuals are so. I am not the equal of Newton, of a blacksmith, nor of Baron Munchausen, judged by intellect, strength and lying-power respectively. What we mean is that our respect and concern for all human beings is, or should be, equal – they are equally members of our species. This is an inspiring idea, but to realize what we really intend when we talk about equality, or equality of opportunity, we need to take the matter further. Prof J. B. S. Haldane has (as so often in such matters) put the thing as sharply as it can be put:

That society enjoys the greatest amount of liberty in which the greatest number of human genotypes can develop their peculiar abilities. It is generally admitted that liberty demands equality of opportunity. It is not equally realized that it demands a variety of opportunities and a tolerance of those who fail to conform to standards which may be culturally desirable but are not essential for the functioning of society.[8]

No society has yet fully solved this one, and our society, which has only now come to recognize the biological as opposed to the ethical side of the problem of equality is actually on the verge of a far bigger crisis than it realizes, precisely as a result of the scientific breakthrough it has made – for it is within measurable distance of abolishing routine work. Streaming of pupils assigned to different intelligence levels was intended originally as an equalitarian move – rich nitwits and poor nitwits would sit in one room, rich and poor geniuses in another. It has not worked that way, in England at least, for extremes of economic position and intelligence are the exception. Most of us are neither very rich, very poor nor very bright, and the emphasis of our tests – as in the case of the Aborigine, who would come off badly by them – is dictated by the fact that intellectuals devised them, and they give prestige to the intellectual's type of performance as white men's tests give prestige to white men. There is an undercurrent already of inequality (in its moral sense) and exasperation in the lower streams of pupils. But this is nothing to what might happen. In our culture, instead of twenty men of varying intelligence being paid £2 each to dig trenches, one man of high technical performance gets £40 with overtime and controls a £50,000 machine. Only a few months ago a lifelong ploughman and tractor driver was refused a driving licence on the ground that the formal intelligence tests showed him to be 'too thick'. Automation will increase the pace of this trend unless we watch it, and an encephalocracy (government by brains for brains) is not a humanly tolerable prospect in view of what we know of the inheritance and distribution of intelligence – which is normally distributed. It is a risk of science that we may let our concern for the highest one-tenth swamp our responsibility to the remaining nine-tenths of ordinary thinkers and doers, once the skills for which we have so long honoured and depended on them can be performed faster by machines. Village society could use frank idiots for simple tasks, and so treat them as equals in the true and social sense. Idiots get in our way – they are safer in institutions. High grade mental defectives can do repetition work – they made surprisingly conscientious NCO's and circuit checkers, not having the initiative to take unauthorized short cuts, but their days are numbered as NCO's have to learn calculus and circuits check themselves. There is a real threat to the lower stream of education that it, too, will become underprivileged through lack of intellectual skills. We have done this before at the race-prejudice level, and we risk repeating an offence to equality at the level of intellectual performance, as against practicality. We do not use the unique skills of the Aborigine, because, coming from the wrong ethnic group, we let him go by default. We may miss the uniqueness of some of our fellow-citizens in the same way, by asking them to do the wrong things, or by failing through our educational system to find out what they can do. Every now and again an ordinary school, containing an ordinarily 'thick' collection of pupils, will flare up like a nova into some quite unexpected skill – tap dancing, amateur radio, producing Macbeth, playing bagpipes – coinciding with the appearance of an enthusiastic teacher with flair. After he leaves it will go back into hibernation – given another moving spirit it will erupt again, with quite a different group of talents. These must all have been latent, one feels, all the time. *'Equality'* in its *true sense consists in evoking them.*

There are some variations in human capacity which are beyond doubt inherited, and in a relatively simple way. Most of these we know concern sensory abilities which can be easily measured.

About twenty years ago the US chemist Arthur L. Fox found that the crystals of a substance called phenylthiocarbamide (PTC) have a bitter taste to some observers, and no taste at all to others. Different people can taste different concentrations of PTC, but by and large the whole population can be divided into tasters and non-tasters. The test is usually done by giving the subject a series of solutions and asking him to sort them into bitter and not bitter; if he does so correctly, the test is repeated at lower and lower concentrations until he cannot distinguish them. There are big geographical and ethnic differences in the proportions of tasters and non-tasters; in European, Australian-European and American populations, about a third are non-tasters – in many non-European peoples the proportion is much

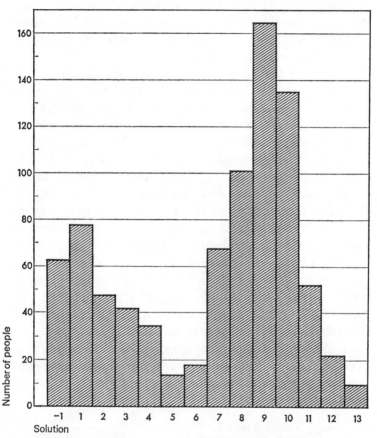

FIG. 3.—Taste threshold of phenylthiocarbamide (PTC) among 855 people was oddly distributed in two peaks. Solution 1 was 1·3 grams of PTC per litre; each number indicates a solution half as strong as the one preceding it.

lower. The genetics of this trait have now been elucidated; it is a typical inherited 'sense-defect'; which, however, is the defect, tasting or non-tasting? There are other sulphur-containing substances which behave in the same way, and there is the odd association that these are nearly all chemicals which inhibit the production of thyroid hormone in the thyroid gland, while nodular goitre of that gland – a disease which occurs where iodine is absent from the water supply – is almost confined to non-tasters. There appears to be some connection here which it would be instructive to work out.

We cannot be sure that PTC tasting is a genetic, or wholly a genetic character. The same applies to other taste and smell sensitivities. We mentioned already that some people have a far higher apparent susceptibility to odours than others – it has been argued that this may involve psychological as well as genetic factors, and complete non-smelling is usually a disease-state due to injury or infection; at the same time industry selects as perfumers only those individuals who have 'nose', and can detect the difference in skin odour between persons of different hair-colour and match this with perfumes; or as tea-tasters and wine-tasters those individuals who can consistently discriminate blends and vintages. In these occupations the number of people who can be successfully trained to do the job required is fairly small compared with the population at large; in other words, the defect is the rule and it looks very much as if genetic as well as environmental factors may be involved.

A more evident trait we class as a sense defect is tone deafness. This does run in families – it is expressed as an almost total inability to reproduce or identify a tune, the characteristic of the gentleman who said:

> 'I know it is odd
> But I cannot tell "God
> Save the Weasel" from "Pop goes the Queen".'

The failure to sing in tune is not a motor defect – the error is in the 'feedback'; the singer cannot hear what he is singing *as* a tune. Tone deafness is therefore an accurate term. It is a handicap, and a hardship to listeners if the subject nonetheless insists on singing, but for social purposes it is no more grave than a mere distaste for music. Far more serious in our culture is the comparable 'deafness' – or blindness – affecting the written word. How far this is genetic we do not know. It is called *alexia* or *dyslexia*; the victim can identify individual letters, as the tone-deaf person can identify sounds, but cannot see a word as a word. He is therefore unable to read, or can read only with difficulty. Such a peculiarity would not be noticed in a non-literate society. In ours, it is a grave disadvantage.

Equally disabling in many contexts is colour blindness, of which there are several forms. Normal people distinguish colour by matching hues in three regions of the spectrum – red, green and blue. Colour-blind people can match or discriminate only two of these and the two commonest defects of this sort, representing defects in two kinds of retinal cell, are probably due to distinct genes. Since both of these are carried on the X chromosome, colour blindness is an example of sex-linked inheritance – occurring in females only exceptionally, but in all males who inherit the appropriate gene.

Here again, red-green confusion might matter little to an Aborigine, but disqualifies a man from several occupations in a society which uses colour as a signal, in traffic lights, on labels, or on railroads. A library recently had its periodical bill payments in chaos; renewal of subscriptions depended on coloured index cards, and the girl in charge was found to be one of the rare female cases of colour blindness.

We detect all these things because they present as disabilities: things most people can do, but a few cannot. There are probably as many genetically determined feats which a few people can do, but most cannot. At present only simple things like double-jointedness, or a keen sense of smell, can be identified like this, but there must be others – some of them potentially important if they could be cultivated. One of the important things about diversity in Man is that it increases his range of activities: as small men make horse jockeys and big men make boxers, so there may be a large matrix of other sporadic abilities which we now cultivate only by accident, or as tricks for entertainment purposes.

There are certain inherited peculiarities which benefit the species by their existence – in certain places and circumstances – but at the price of mischief to the individual. These are recessive genetic faults which cause disease or death when inherited from both parents, but some unexpected advantage when present in a half-dose only. The most thoroughly proven of these is the gene which causes sickle-shaped red blood corpuscles. These are disadvantageous, and the inheritor of the sickling gene from both parents is a sick man. The man who inherits it from one parent only, however, has a noticeably higher resistance to malaria parasites attacking his red cells, and since single doses (heterozygy) will always be commoner than double (homozygy), the sickling gene has 'proved advantageous' and persists in malarious areas of Africa – but is much rarer elsewhere. Another blood-cell altering gene, that for the disease thalassaemia, is found chiefly but not exclusively in areas round the Mediterranean which are or were malarious; in the double dose it is nearly lethal – in the single, it must presumably (though this is an inference from its distribution) act as does the gene for sickling.

Even where no such clear-cut special advantage is concerned however, there is a general tendency for persons with unlike genes from each parent to be fitter (hybrid vigour) both in the common and the evolutionary sense than those who have many gene-pairs alike. It is a common trick in farming to cross two rather weakly but stable pure lines, and then sell the large, vigorous, fertile and quick-growing hybrid offspring. Most recessive genes which are lethal in a double dose, or at least disadvantageous, probably contribute more vigour to the *species* through this action of increasing genic diversity than they cause mischief, grave though that mischief may be to the man who is dealt an unlucky genetic hand.

We no longer cheerfully accept (or most of us no longer cheerfully accept) the crass heritability of behaviour such as crime, alcoholism or fitness to govern. In a sense it is odd, by mammalian standards, that the nineteenth-century Italian criminologist Lombroso was wrong in his account of 'criminal' or, for that matter, innately virtuous, types, identifiable by 'signs of degeneracy' or the reverse – many quirks of animal behaviour are heritable, and one can breed for them as one makes a cocktail, by a simple process of mixture. Thus in dog-breeding one can introduce traits such as 'nobility' (which means, as often as not, going into water to retrieve any object from a duck to a drowning person) pointing, clapping (the trick performed by sheepdogs which run towards the sheep and then squat down), grinning, gun-shyness and many others. All one can say to the theoretical proposition that behavioural tricks in Man are also heritable is that culture and learning so swamp this built-in type of behaviour that it is never certainly identifiable. Adopted children have many of their adoptive parents' mannerisms. Nor is it enough to prove that in our society a particular kind of personality, presumed to be partly genetic in origin, is more prone to commit crimes, vote Conservative, or play the fiddle professionally – nor even that twins resemble each other most in such attributes when they are identical. It would be useful predictively to know of such correlations, if true, but in a different culture the crook might be the musician, and the musician the stern traditionalist. The most one can say is that some persons appear innately unmusical because tone deaf, and others innately musical from the fact that, however little encouraged, they write or play music at a ridiculously early age. A good sort of society would be the one which gave harmless expression to the maximum number of such divergent abilities.

The final manifestation of human diversity is individual identity. We are all different, but all save identical twins are chemically different. Every so often a respected and useful citizen, who should have had several more years of work ahead of him, dies because a minute clot obstructs an artery in his heart. If he had been a bicycle or an omnibus, we could have renewed the defective part as soon as we saw that it was about to fail. Why, one might ask, apart from the difficulty of obtaining a healthy heart to replace an unserviceable one, can we not do this in Man?

Surgically speaking, the replacement of organs is perfectly feasible. I have seen Dr Demichov, Moscow, exchange hearts and lungs between two dogs and have them running about within hours of the operation. Even the problem of supply is not insuperable – we already have bone banks and blood banks which maintain stocks of spares for use in emergencies, and there is even the more distant possibility of growing isolated organs for use as replacements. The trouble lies in the fact of our identity. Unless we are identical twins who started life as a single individual, every one of us differs from every other one in chemical constitution, and the protective immunity-system in our bodies rejects foreign cells and rapidly destroys them. Unless they were twins, Demichov's dogs would live only a few hours – after which the grafted hearts or lungs would die. There have been tragic cases where in spite of this knowledge a parent or brother has given a kidney to be implanted in a person dying of kidney failure – for a few days it has taken but unless the donor is a twin, sooner or later the implanted organ has died, and its host with it.

Human individuals differ in their tissue antigens, as in their blood-group antigens, and the number of systems involved is so great that no two individuals are ever wholly alike in this respect. Chemical individuality is the final expression of human genetic variation – beyond that, we vary from environmental causes only.

This is the reason that unless I have a twin, identical with me, who is willing to part with an organ I may need, I cannot be repaired by grafting. There are exceptions. A particularly fortunate one is the cornea, obtained from the eyeball of a dead man, which can be grafted, with complete restoration of sight. The reason that a cornea will take in this way is probably that it has no direct blood supply, so that the normal immunity mechanisms do not attack it. Grafting of other tissues such as bone marrow is sometimes possible when the immunity system has been knocked out by a massive dose of radiation. This fact has been used to treat diseases of the blood, and the lives of several Yugoslav engineers who were accidentally injured by radiation from an atomic pile were saved in this way by French biologists a short while ago. The skin grafts, incidentally, which are used to treat burns, are of two kinds – either they are taken from another part of the same individual (the thigh or the abdomen) to repair damage in important areas like hand and face – in which case, since they are part of the patient already, they take without difficulty: or they are taken from a donor, and are only temporary, acting as a very effective kind of dressing, which is rejected or replaced as healing continues. Blood is another special case, for the red blood cells, which are the object of giving a transfusion, have no nuclei, and provided that they are correctly chosen they are not destroyed by the recipient, though the white cells that go with them are.

In animals, especially mice, experimental grafting is relatively easy, because by prolonged inbreeding we have produced mice as alike as twins, which can and do accept grafts from one another. In all countries biologists are working on grafting problems, partly to see if the difficulty of using spare parts in Man can be got round, and partly because the production of a chimera (an animal which carries organs or parts derived from another individual) is a most useful tool in understanding processes of immunity, of ageing, of tumour production and of development generally.

The key to one possible way round the problem of the homograft reaction, as this sloughing-off process is called, comes from the study of cattle. It was noticed that grafts took between twin calves which differed in sex and could not, therefore, be identical twins. Cattle were known to have the unusual feature that the blood supply in the mother's womb is shared by twin embryos even when they are not identical, and cells are able to pass from one embryo to another. Starting from this observation, biologists found that if cells are injected into an embryo mouse before it is born, that embryo loses the power to throw off grafts of similar cells in adult life. A black mouse, injected before birth with white mouse cells, will accept grafts of white mouse skin in later life.

Teams in several countries are now trying by various means either to overcome the homograft reaction or to detect the antibodies and other chemical substances involved. The possibility of using this work to find out the nature of the differences between human individuals is quite likely to be more important in the long run than any direct application to the matter of spare parts.

Chapter 5

Hazards and Enemies

IT IS only when an astronaut goes into space that he realizes how well he is adapted to his environment on earth, and how thoroughly that environment protects him. Only a few thousand feet up, he requires to carry oxygen with him to enable him to breathe. A little higher, and he requires protection from the intense ultraviolet light emitted by the sun. Higher still, and he encounters dangerous radiation from the same source. If he were not protected by a capsule, he would also be exposed to roasting on his sunward side and freezing on his shaded side. At the same time, he would be free of one risk which he has always faced without recognizing it – that of competition from other creatures. So far as we know, there are no other living things in outer space.

Life as we know it needs the very narrow range of conditions which occur on the surface of the earth. This is to be expected, since it is an evolutionary product of those conditions; for all we know, other conditions might produce some quite different phenomenon analogous to life. Different forms of life, too, are fitted into different niches in the variable environment which exists on earth. All require protection from extremes of temperature and radiation and from lack or excess of oxygen and metabolites, but some are more catholic in their tastes, or more adaptable, than others. Man is one of the most successfully adaptable – partly through his ability to act intelligently and alter his environment, but also through his basic physiological capacity. He has survived at least one Ice Age, at a relatively early stage of his civilization; he has colonized the whole of the earth's surface except the extreme poles, some deserts, and the highest mountains, and the only place he has not reached with mechanical protection is the extreme bottom of the sea. The only organisms with a similar range are some of the hardy bacteria, and even they are not fully active in all these environments. Possibly the next most successful mammal is the rat, and this has spread partly or wholly with the assistance of Man.

In meeting this range of environmental needs, and the huge diversity of social patterns, ranging from urban to nomadic and from Eskimo to rain-forest Pygmy, which go with them, Man has been helped both by social and intellectual behaviour and by genetic variation.

The hazards specifically due to *climate*, if one takes that in its widest sense, are the hazards of heat, cold, deprivation of water and high altitude. Excessive damp, in tropical rain forests, is not a hazard *per se* – such forests are a fair habitat for Man, and if they are unhealthy for the unacclimatized, this is chiefly due to the fact that they have a rich fauna of all kinds, including parasites, and a rich flora including bacteria.

Given clothing, Man copes well with severe dry cold, though if this is accompanied by wind, his extremities soon become frostbitten. He copes equally well with dry heat, remaining active through his efficient sweating system. Wet heat can induce heatstroke, but even in the hottest and most humid places and seasons, local (as opposed to visiting) Man has usually adapted his way of life, his degree of activity, and his form of housing to accommodate it. High altitude is more interesting. Men live habitually at over 13,000 ft in the Puna de Heatama (Andes); for this purpose they have to produce excessive numbers of red blood corpuscles and a high level of blood haemoglobin – outsiders take a longish time to acclimatize to these levels, and highlanders to the plains. High altitude populations are also exposed to a sizeable increase in ultraviolet and ionizing radiation – the first increases the incidence of skin cancer in exposed parts; the second does not seem to have any very marked effect on fertility or longevity, though it might be expected to increase the overall mutation rate. Apart from this effect of altitude, excessive radiation exposure is confined to peoples living on radioactive rocks, as in parts of Kerala (S. India), and to town-dwellers in civilized countries who make excessive medical use of x-rays.

There are a few climatic emergencies with which Man has difficulty in coping; these include unexpected droughts or floods which destroy food supplies. A sudden change in the climatic distribution of ice (an Ice Age, that is, of fairly quick onset, say 10–20,000 years) would probably lead to widespread changes in population behaviour rather than in a world-wide climatic extermination of Man, even if no technical resources for keeping the climate of cities and houses steady were available. Cities can now be built, if necessary, at the North Pole. Melting of ice would be a more serious matter, for it would submerge large areas. Other less manageable climatic events are those which are themselves catastrophic – volcanic eruption, earthquake and storm. All these, though lethal, are fortunately too local or infrequent to threaten the species – though a massive earthquake in a civilized urban country unused to such events could easily kill millions if it were to occur on a wide enough scale. The only climatic catastrophe which might conceivably suddenly kill a large part of the human race is the impact of a very large meteorite, especially if it fell in the sea and produced a tidal wave of large enough dimensions, for Man is largely a coast-, valley- and plain-dweller, at least so far as his cities are concerned.

Though genetic factors may play a part in making the men of different regions adaptable, by varying build, colour, stature and the like, and favouring round squat men in cold places and long thin men in hot, by far the greatest part of our adaptibility is behavioural. The Australian Bushman differs physically from the European, but not very much physiologically – yet he can survive in desert where even an equipped white man might die, partly through adaptation (Australian investigators who slept naked in a Bushman camp were perpetually woken by cold, while their hosts slept soundly) but still more through knowledge and way of life. He will *know* where food and water are obtainable in unobvious forms, and he will *behave* in a manner adapted to the peculiar kind of setting around him. Europeans in India used to die of heatstroke from inappropriate clothing and inappropriate habits.

Great attempts used to be made to relate civilization to climate – usually with the conclusion that the temperate climate of Europe and America, in which the authors wrote, was the most conducive to progress. There is something in the theory, however, that temperate and changeable weather, without great or long-drawn-out excesses of heat and cold, is favourable to the growth of active industrial nations – if only that it is in these climates that such nations have so far developed. One could endlessly descant on the effects of individual climates on individual civilizations – how, for example, the severe winter and the prolonged muddy spring and summer in the Russian plain led to a combination of centralized and decentralized political power, or how the rice economy has determined the structure of society in large parts of the East: the only climatic factor which has effectively destroyed whole civilizations is probably drought.

Man has probably the most efficient heat-loss mechanism of any animal – in dry air, he can sit quietly in an air temperature which will fry an egg – but very little resource against cold. Being hairless, and able to get warm only by work or shivering, he has had to devise clothes. If he performs well in temperate and (with fire) cold regions, this is probably an added accomplishment. Almost certainly his original milieu is a temperature steady around 70° F.

The zeal of older medical climatologists such as Dr Huntington for the 'energy' obtainable by living in a temperate climate might now be moderated, in favour of the advantages of a quieter tempo of life. Clarence Mills attempted to investigate the effects of climate on the activity of rats under cool (18° C), moderate (29° C) and hot (33° C) régimes. The coolest group were large, fast growing, fast developing, perpetually hungry, fertile and intelligent; they were also subject to cancer, which grew as rapidly as they did. The hottest group were sluggish, apathetic, slow to sex and develop, and not conspicuously intelligent at learning-tests – but they were almost cancer-proof, and lived into old age. As Prof Dudley Stamp remarks: 'It is time there was some new thinking about life and living in the tropics. The absence of any built-in mechanism for resistance to cold, the absence of fur, for example, suggests that Man is naturally a tropical animal.' We should hasten to add that what is less easy to maintain under hot conditions is not *intelligence*, which nobody could deny to tropical Man, but motivation – or, in our culture, what the Hindu observer would see as purposeless, compulsive over-activity. With air conditioning, the civilizations of the future may conceivably get the best of both worlds.

A hundred years ago, our predecessors might well, on Biblical grounds, have cited 'flood' as the main climatic hazard to Man. We should now be much more inclined to name drought – as the least-surmountable barrier to survival over large parts of the earth. Flood has certainly impressed itself deeply on human thinking, for many traditions have their flood-legends. That in the Bible is very like the version found in the Babylonian epic of Gilgamesh. Many not over-profitable attempts have been made to work out what real climatic event, if any, survives in these stories. Change in the course of the Nile or the Euphrates and the filling of the Mediterranean basin all have had their adherents. What is more to the point, perhaps, is that flood legends are common, and floods have been considered as divine judgments, *because* Man persistently lived in flood-susceptible areas. Floods, in fact, with the rich soil they bring down, have been the price he had to pay for alluvial agriculture like that of Egypt or China, where fertile floodless years alternated with destructive flooding, when the providing river-god became angry and intractable. This has been the pattern in many old civilizations, and the climatic hazard of flood was one that had to be endured until the era of dam building and hydroelectric power generation. Man has been very largely a flood-plain animal since he began to farm.

We know of several local cultures which appear, for one reason or another, to have run out of water. Petra, which is visited by tourists today, and the 'lost' Indian cities, such as Fatehpur-Sikri, may have been abandoned for this reason. There is a not-over-distant risk of some of the world's big cities going the same way in the future. Angry waterless farmers in California have been known to bomb the aqueducts carrying water to fill the baths and swimming pools of Los Angeles. The energetic irrigation plans of the Israelis have had to be adjusted to the fall in the water table, which risked bringing in salt and fouling the supply. We may find cheap methods of desalting, but these are likely to be of limited application only in the face of the huge water requirements of modern civilizations. It will be interesting to see how our habits are affected in the future by the need to keep these requirements down.

It is fortunate that so far in history climatic swings affecting rainfall have been relatively slow, although years of drought and years of excessive rain have left their mark in the size of the annual rings we see in fossil wood. Some abnormally narrow rings are probably due to sunless years, resulting, it has been suggested, from large amounts of volcanic dust following a major eruption – others are probably evidence of droughts.

Drought may also have been a force behind some of the great migrations – it has been argued that the Jews left Egypt *because* the Nile (not the Red Sea) dried up. The Mayan migration and the rapid spread of Islam under Mohammed have also been put down to a world rain shortage over the period concerned (these, one might add, are not theories about which climatologists or historians are now very enthusiastic).

If invaders did not flee from drought, however, they certainly spread it. The destruction of the civilization in Mediterranean North Africa by successive invasions, first by the Vandals and much later (in the seventh century) by the Arabs, was followed by the destruction of irrigation channels and wells, and the invasion of the sand. Hannibal got his elephants not from the remote south, but from forests occupying a part of what is now the Sahara. They were still there when Paulinus described them in AD 47, but later inhabitants cut them down. Man is one of his own gravest hazards in the field of climate; he is liable to create deserts by soil erosion, tree felling, keeping goats and by the over-use of water, and these hazards are by no means at an end. Water may prove to be the limiting factor in the growth of our cities, and even modern methods of climatic control now being developed may, without careful international planning, recoil either on those who carry them out or on their neighbours.

We shall several times have to point out that one important element in Man's 'hostile' environment has been his fellow Man and himself – 'l'enfer, c'est les autres'. No other animal has struck quite this ecological balance between the advantages and the disadvantages of a complex social mode of behaviour – between what Kropotkin called, in its biological, social and political contexts, 'mutual aid', and mutual mischief. Another dangerous force has been Man's own ingenuity or energy when unaccompanied by foresight or when driven by psychopathology; radioactive fallout is an example of the second – rash meddling with climate for experimental or even philanthropic reasons might yet be an example of the first. No nation should ever again be allowed to undertake any project which threatens the human environment. It is too much to hope that such proposals will not be made, but not too much to hope that they will be put down by common agreement. Meanwhile atomic waste, and the occasional 'lost' bomb, are cheerfully dumped in the sea, on which we shall soon depend for food.

Man shares the 'biosphere' with other men, and with other organisms. In each case he cannot do without these neighbours, but may find himself in conflict or competition with them. Apart from a few mineral poisons or deficiencies, the hazards of human life are almost all traceable to this need to coexist with other living forms. High among the possible blunders likely to damage the biosphere we must put extermination-mania; the idea that one of our plant or animal companions has reached a point at which its continued presence is intolerable. Some are indeed intolerable – malaria mosquitos or gypsy moths, for example – but the attempt to 'exterminate' such pests with poisons, rather than to control them, usually leads to widespread damage to other forms. Moreover some of the chemicals used are now so active that the possibility of serious accident is one to be considered. This need not be accident to Man – a total kill of birds or insects in any district would have far-reaching ill effects on food supplies and the environment generally. The two greatest biotopic sins are to try to exterminate something by an indiscriminate method, and to introduce something – even something harmless like watercress – into an environment where it may spread and be a nuisance. The rabbit in Australia, the grey squirrel in England, the giant snail all round the tropics, and the water hyacinth in Africa, are all examples of a delinquency of this kind.

The *plants*, with one vast exception, are not competitors of Man so much as neighbours or servants. When they do him harm it is usually incidental or accidental. Thorns must have been one of the oldest enemies of any hairless primate, and come in all sizes from the vast barbs of *Euphorbia spinosissima* and the giant cacti to the hairs of cowitch, which set up intolerable itching. Many break off and set up poisoning, others, like the stinging hairs of the nettle, inject histamine-like substances. One nettle, from Timor, *U. urentissima*, has a sting reputedly so severe as to produce many days' illness, and even suicide from the acute pain.

The most spectacular noxious plants, to Man and cattle, are those which are poisonous on ingestion. Hemlock poisoned Socrates; children die regularly from laburnum seeds eaten as 'beans' – there is prussic acid in laurel, and meat cooked on oleander sticks has been known to prove fatal.

Plant poisons are widespread and very diverse. They tend to run in families, such as the Solanaceae, which includes belladonna, stramonium, tobacco and hyoscyamus, as well as potato (the berries of which are poisonous) and tomato; or the various species of *Strychnos*. The noxious chemical substances in plants are of many kinds, from simple poisons such as prussic acid, released by hydrolysis from a glucoside, to the very complicated plant alkaloids, many of which are medicinal, and among the most useful of all substances when applied to palliate disease.

The function of these poisonous ingredients in the plant is not at all clear. One might expect them to be protective, in rendering the leaves distasteful or noxious to animals – yet many of the most important enemies of such plants are immune: the poisons which interest us in plants are naturally those which affect Man – if pests are their target such protective toxins ('phytoncides') are only partially effective: snails feed freely on deadly nightshade (they are insusceptible to atropine) and the oleander hawk moth larva on oleander. A great many of the physiologically active alkaloids in plants are not poisonous, or not present in sufficient amount to be so – caffeine in tea plants, for example – and there are many chemically similar but quite inactive alkaloids. It is hard to believe that there is *no* evolutionary connection between the presence of active alkaloids in plants and their physiological effects on mammals; one such plant-mammal link is already recognized, in the springtime 'surge' of oestrogenic substances in pasture, which helps to time the breeding season of cattle. But the nature of the link in other cases is much less clear.

Be that as it may, Man has been remarkably successful in finding out activity in unlikely places – there are few poisonous plants which he has not recognized, and often used as medicaments, arrow poisons and the like. He has been equally successful with the useful non-poisonous alkaloids; tea, coffee and maté (Ilex paraguayensis) are the only known sources of

93

caffeine in quantity, and all three have been used as beverages since antiquity. In the same way, he has learned to make widespread use of the deliriants and intoxicants – mescal, cocaine, peyote, soma, opium, hemp – in spite of, or rather because of, their mental effects. Wise women and witch-doctors past and present, must have done much deliberate investigation by trial and error, at considerable personal risk.

Even more remarkable are the instances where Man has learned to process and use potentially poisonous plant food. The unripe ackee fruit contains a substance with a poisonous, insulin-like action – the ripe fruit is wholesome, but poisoning in children is not uncommon from impatience in waiting for it to ripen. The most striking example of this kind, however, is manioc (cassava) which is edible only after being freed of its highly poisonous juice. One must wonder how this was found out, and how so potentially dangerous a plant became a staple source of food.

The fungi are a notorious source both of deliriants and of poisons, and fungus poisoning is probably the commonest cause of death from plant toxins throughout Europe. In England, where only the culinary mushroom is popularly considered 'wholesome', there are still deaths – the vast majority of them from the death cap (Amanita phalloides) which does not closely resemble a field mushroom, and a few from such unlikely fungi as the bright-red and spotted A. muscaria (Fly agaric) which used to be used as fly poison, or the rarer Inocybe patouillardi, which has sealing-wax red juice. Toadstool-eating nations are better briefed on the identification of fungi, but deaths still occur from a variety of poisonous fungi.

A much more insidious fungus poison is that which causes spurring of rye. Batches of rye containing spurred grains infected with the ergot fungus have given rise to epidemics throughout history, and even in recent times. Ergotism produces abortion and gangrene of the extremities, but these are preceded by acute mental symptoms. Some of the outbursts of 'dancing mania', of panic, and of religious hysteria in the Middle Ages have been put down to ergotism, but recent outbreaks are rare.

In August 1951, many people in the village of Pont St Esprit near Montpellier became ill – first with nausea, sensations of coldness, and difficulty in swallowing, later with insomnia and with delirium coming on towards evening. The patients were affected with symptoms very like those of the alcoholic 'horrors' (delirium tremens) – they saw flames and animals, were haunted by unreasonable remorse and guilt, had delusions that they were in Hell, and two threw themselves out of windows. In all, of twenty-five delirious cases, four died. This was a typical outbreak of the 'mal des ardents', so often described in graphic terms by medieval writers. The source of these symptoms was a batch of ergot-infested rye flour.

It seized upon men with a twitching and a kind of benumbedness in the hands and feet, sometimes on one side, sometimes the other, sometimes both. Hence a convulsion invaded men as they went about their daily employments...until the sick would lie down and roll up their bodies into a ball; terrible pains made the sick to shriek and yell... (Sennertus, De Febribus, 1658)

In medieval cases convulsive symptoms were less common than gangrene – we read that in 994 thousands in Aquitaine suffered the burning off of their limbs by invisible fire, through the wrath of God, while others had fits and seizures – almost certainly a description of epidemic ergotism.

Lastly there are plants which strike by remote action, those which produce allergy. Some people are made ill by contact with primula or strawberries; up to half the population are severely burned by handling the various poisonous species of sumach (poison oak, poison ivy), or even by the smoke of burning woodland where these grow. There are thus different degrees of commonness for these various allergic diseases; among the commonest is allergy to pollen – grass pollen, chiefly, in Europe, where hay fever is a spring complaint, and ragweed pollen in America, where it occurs in Autumn. The incidence and severity of asthma, rhinitis and skin disorders due to these plants rises and falls with the pollen count, which is now published as a warning to known allergic subjects to take precautions. Many other flower pollens affect susceptible people. Pollen is the agent, chiefly because it is the only part of the plant which yields fine airborne particles. Most people know the legend of the Upas tree, which poisoned anything which came in its shade. The nearest factual approach to this among plants dangerous to Man is the poison oak or the poison ivy, which injure susceptible people on the slightest skin contact, or even contact with rain which has fallen on their leaves. The results are usually painful, however, not fatal.

Another extraordinary allergy is *favism* – illness with blood in the urine, dizziness and fever following exposure to the odour and pollen of flowering broad beans. This is due to a recessive gene – sufferers are short of an enzyme. Yet another is the mystery illness of children coeliac disease, which claimed a great many victims with wasting, anaemia and persistent fatty diarrhoea; not many years ago, such children used to be reared almost wholly on bananas and apple pulp – if they reached adult life they usually recovered, but not all did reach it. During the war, shortage excluded wheat flour from the diet in parts of Europe, and with its disappearance the cases recovered. On the return of white bread they fell ill again. Coeliac disease is an allergy to wheat gluten, and even the small traces of flour present in canned meat and soup are enough to induce it.

All other harmful plant influences, however, pale before the bacteria. These omnipresent living things, classed as 'plants' in juxtaposition to the fungi for want of a better place to put them, have overthrown dynasties, and could still, by an unlucky mutation, kill off the species. Or so one might infer – yet Man has survived their attacks so far, albeit in smaller populations than those of today's big cities, and, indeed, as with all other neighbours in the biosphere, he is unable to do without them. Germ-free mammals and chicks have now been reared, but they are poor things – most creatures depend on bacterial guests to provide some part of their nutritional requirements, for the bacteria are virtuoso organic chemists, and can synthesize many things that vertebrate cells cannot. They maintain the fertility of the soil, break down refuse, fix nitrogen and form vitamins. Only a small fraction are rogues and injure Man by attacking him directly as parasites like plague, cholera, pneumonia or gonorrhoea, by producing toxins in food which he eats, like the botulism bacillus, or by growing in his body and releasing highly active poisons there, like the germs of tetanus or diphtheria. Once again we must be selective – if we sterilized the world of bacteria we should probably abolish ourselves. It is this relatively small group of pathogens which we must learn to control, and are in fact controlling.

There is no space here to discuss all the bacteria dangerous to Man – of these, however, the most deadly have been those which have been capable of explosive spread, either by taking the same route as the allergy-producing pollens and spreading through the air, in droplets coughed out by infected people, or by contaminating water, as typhoid and cholera do, or by travelling through the bites of insects or other vectors, like bubonic plague. This disease of black rats, spread by fleas to Man, is a measure not only of the success of the bacterium (Pasteurella pestis) but of the rat, which is a constant companion of Man on his journeys by sea and in his settlements and granaries. Not many bacteria are in fact spread by insect or other arthropod bites – the diseases so carried are chiefly due to protozoa or viruses; typhus, spread by louse-bites, and a killer next only to plague, is due to an organism *incertae sedis* known as a rickettsia. Other diseases spread, as we have said, in food and water contaminated by the excreta of sick men or animals. Some are animal diseases, the germs of which appear in milk (Malta fever, tuberculosis) and are passed on to Man. All these are invasive organisms, i.e. they actively multiply in the body and may invade the blood and tissues. Some others, such as diphtheria or tetanus, multiply little in the body, or remain in one site only, but the chemical toxin which they produce is intensely poisonous and kills their host. Yet others never need enter the body at all – they have done their work beforehand, by growing in food and producing poisons in it. The staphylococcus which produces enterotoxin is a germ of this kind. When we read of a whole opera party taken from the theatre to hospital in a fleet of ambulances after eating cold salmon, this germ's toxin is usually the cause. Botulism, caused by eating food tainted by the botulism organism, is due to poisoning with one of the most active poisons known, formed by the bacterium in the absence of air (and investigated of late by pathogenic human beings, for there are such, as a possible weapon of war).

Many bacteria, fortunately enough, die quickly away from the human body, and do not persist. Among the persistent are those which form almost indestructible spores – anthrax in particular, which can lie dormant in ivory or bones or soil almost indefinitely.

One bacterial disease, gonorrhoea, is spread by sexual intercourse, together with two other disease agents, one a virus (lymphogranuloma venereum) and the other a spirochaete (syphilis). Spirochaetes, cause of syphilis and yaws, are corkscrew-shaped organisms usually classed with the bacteria.

The conquest of the bacterial diseases, which began with Pasteur and Ehrlich and still continues, is quite the most important change in the human environment since prehistory. It has altered Man's whole outlook. These diseases have been controlled first by recognizing their modes of spread and cutting chains of infection through sewage into food and water, by immunization, and latterly by the use of specific drugs (chemotherapy). Strangely enough, in this field it is to the toxins produced by fungi to kill competing fungi and bacteria that we have had to turn for remedies against disease – penicillin, erythromycin, streptomycin, terramycin, tyrothricin and many other bacteria-killing agents are substances of this sort elaborated by moulds, or chemical derivates modelled on these natural bacteria-killers. It was only with Fleming's classic observation that we began to take note of this phenomenon of antibiotic production, and take advantage of the means used by moulds to secure themselves against bacterial competition. The small part which some mould-like organisms play in human disease – in causing the horrible but luckily rare disease actinomycosis, for example, which riddles its possessor with abscesses – has thus been amply counterpoised by their utility to medicine.

While the deadly bacteria, which cause large-scale epidemics, and to which most of us have little initial resistance, have been the great mass destroyers of Man, some of the most grievous diseases as well as the most socially important are the work of organisms to which we have strong resistance as a species, so that they are only just pathogenic for us; chief among these are the germs of leprosy and tuberculosis. The cholera vibrio either kills us or leaves us immune – the tubercle bacillus may cause acute death in children, but more often, before the advent of chemotherapy, tuberculosis and leprosy were lifelong battles with an organism which could not kill outright, but could not be killed by the body. Syphilis is another disease which has 'drawn its match' with Man in this way; in Europe when it first was introduced from South America, and in Pacific island communities where it was transmitted by sailors, it spread at first like a pestilence – but with the passage of time, populations became progressively immune. 'Civilization is syphilization': arsenicals and penicillin apart, we no longer see the florid cases or the gross after-effects described in nineteenth-century medical textbooks. It is in curing these chronic infections that chemotherapy has scored its second biggest triumph.

Contrary to popular belief in the last century, relatively few large *animals* normally prey on Man – it is Man who preys on the majority of other animals (even on large inedible carnivores, for their hides). Most big cats, and animals such as the hyaena, will attack children or stragglers – few prey deliberately on Man as such, especially Man in organized groups. Indeed, many of the animals most dangerous to Man are so because he comes into their territory and is mistaken for a rival (by the bull or the rhinoceros, for example) or even for a mate – it is said that the male moose will display to a Man as to a female, with consequences as dangerous as those of aggression. None of the more bellicose larger animals – bull, wild pig, bear, rhino, etc. – *prey* on Man, and even the tiger and leopard rarely do so, though they may take advantage of an occasional opportunity.

Man accordingly falls foul of animals (1) when they prey on him – sharks are about the best example of this kind of predation; (2) when he gets in the way of their territorial or other behaviour; (3) when their means of passive defence are particularly devastating for him, as with nearly all the venomous animals, hardly any of which – except perhaps ants – could be said to be able to prey on Man. Beside these directly harmful groups, where mischief results from an encounter, there are two others, the parasites and the vectors of parasites. We will deal with these in order.

We have said that sharks are among the only true predators on Man – meaning that they actively feed on him given the opportunity. Pliny mentions the 'cruel combat of sponge fishers' against the 'dog fish' – and incidentally noted that they can be scared off by swimming straight at them. Rondelet, the Renaissance medical naturalist, describes how one chased his footman up the beach until he had the presence of mind to kick it to death! Later writers debated whether sharks preferred coloured or white men (observation actually suggests that they most often attack light-coloured objects) and how far the slave trade 'taught' them anthropophagous tastes. In this welter of speculative natural history, it is only lately – during the war, in fact, which exposed aircrew and shipping survivors to shark attack on a large scale – that serious work has been done on the subject, especially in the field of repellents. These are effective up to a point against the single lone fish, but not against sharks *en masse* under 'mob feeding' conditions. Of all large animals which are palpably enemies of Man in the ordinarily accepted and conversational sense, sharks unquestionably kill most people. Leopards and the various species of alligator and crocodile probably come next.

It is interesting that there is often considerable dispute as to *which* animals are really venomous. Apart from imaginary enemies like the basilisk and the Tatzelwurm, which obviously belong to the field of magic and mythology, Man both attributes dangerous powers to animals which have none and (possibly as a result of scientific scepticism) has failed to credit that some venomous creatures really are so. We are not over-sensible in knowing our enemies, though we are losing the nineteenth-century prejudice that every animal, as well as every 'primitive' nation, is apt to attack us on sight.

In 1798 Donovan wrote:

Travellers agree that the temperate parts of Asia would be a terrestrial paradise, were it not for the multitude of troublesome insects and reptiles.... In a well-cultivated country such as China, many of these creatures can scarcely find shelter: but such as harbour in the walls or furniture of human dwellings are as abundant in that as in any country that lies within or near the Tropics. Amongst the latter, none produce more terrible effects than the centipede, whose poison is as venomous as that of the scorpion.

The love of a good story and a spectacular stinging animal has done much to confuse Man as to his really important enemies. The anopheles mosquito, which also enters houses, was a far greater drawback to the temperate subtropics than any centipede, but it was less conspicuous. The centipede can bite, however; an English zoology student who was bitten by one in the south of France in 1949 had a swollen hand like that from a hornet sting. The effects had quite passed off in three days.

The real animal enemies of Man are the parasites and their allies the vectors. Vast numbers of species can be parasitic on Man, and journals of parasitology perpetually describe new mites and new worms. The species involved may range in size from the tapeworm many feet long to the minute organisms of malaria or leishmaniasis. As we carry living bacteria in our intestine, we carry animals on our body surface – if these do harm we call them parasites, otherwise they are mere guests, or commensals. The threadworm often found in human intestines is a borderline case – harmless in small numbers (most of us have a few) but likely to cause some itching if it is very numerous. Even the cleanest of us harbour mites as commensals, living on the wax of our ears; the mites of scabies, however, burrow in the skin and produce severe irritation and rashes ('the itch'). Lice are so common in primates that we should regard them as near-commensals, even though they suck blood, if they did not also act as disease-carriers, especially of typhus.

Parasites may gain access to us in many ways – by arrival

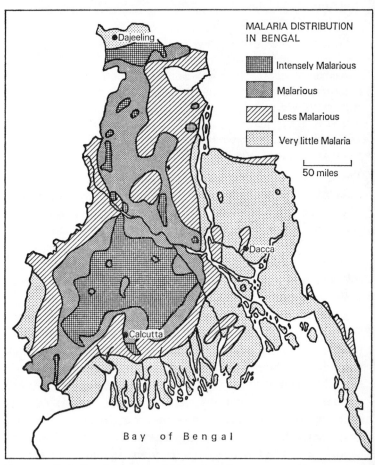

FIG. 4.—C. A. Bentley's map of Malaria in Bengal, *c.* 1910.

on the skin (fleas, lice) by being swallowed, either as eggs or as larvae (many parasitic worms), by piercing the skin (larvae of the hookworms and guineaworm), or by being injected by the bite of an insect, itself parasitic on Man – louse, mosquito or bug. Insect-borne diseases are among the world's greatest scourges. Those due to animal parasites include malaria (plasmodium), sleeping sickness (trypanosome), kala-azar (leishmania), fly sickness of cattle (trypanosome), elephantiasis (nematode) and others of lesser note. There is one equally important insect-borne virus disease, namely yellow fever.

While the bacterial diseases slay their thousands directly, the protozoan and metazoan parasites do so indirectly. Being usually chronic in their effects, they stunt the health and economic development of entire nations. If we could wave a wand in the interests of human happiness and abolish three diseases completely, no public health expert would have much difficulty in selecting which three – malaria, hookworm and bilharzia. They account for more chronic ill health, more social apathy, more inability to work, and more consequent mal-nutrition than any others. Malaria, as everyone now knows, is spread not by 'foul air' but by the bite of a mosquito which has bitten an infected person, spreading the plasmodia from one blood stream to the other. Untreated, it drags on with recurrent fever and anaemia – it can also kill acutely. Fig. 5 shows the rural depopulation of Bengal and the distribution of malaria at the start of the present century. This pattern has been repeated elsewhere. Before the advent of mosquito control and the anti-malarial drugs, whole fertile regions were uninhabitable, and swamps could not be drained, by reason of malaria. Since anti-malarial measures were taken, Sardinia is on its way to becoming a tourist resort. Northern Ceylon, which is full of the ruins of elaborate medieval cultures, was left uninhabited for centuries because of malaria. Campaigns for its elimination have been in hand under WHO for several years, aiming at control of mos-quitoes and elimination of parasites from the blood of cases (so that mosquitoes cannot reach them).

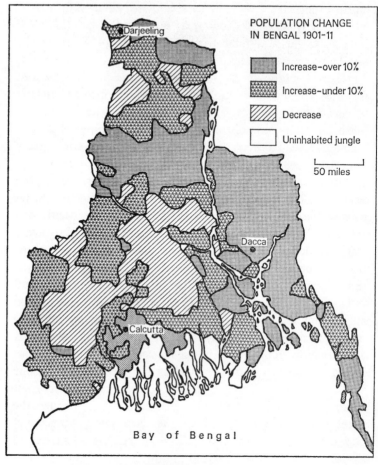

POPULATION CHANGE
IN BENGAL 1901-11

Increase–over 10%

Increase–under 10%

Decrease

Uninhabited jungle

50 miles

Darjeeling

Dacca

Calcutta

Bay of Bengal

FIG. 5.—Rural depopulation in Bengal, 1910–11.

Hookworm (ankylostomiasis) is another chronic debilitating disease, less grave than malaria in its effects on life, but no less grave in its effects on well-being; it is due to vast numbers of minute worms infesting the intestinal wall, sucking blood, and causing intense apathy and debility. This is a disease of countries where faeces contaminated with the eggs of hookworms are allowed to lie about near houses. The eggs hatch and produce larvae which pierce the skin of the feet and ankles – it is rare in people who wear shoes. Re-infection is continuous. With proper hygiene new cases soon cease to appear. This disease disappears when the earth closet goes.

Bilharzia (schistosomiasis) is widespread over tropical Africa, Asia and America. It probably ranks next to malaria as a source of chronic illness and debility, and like malaria it is truly pandemic – everyone in many areas is infected to the point of illness. Bilharzia is typical of many parasitic diseases of Man and of animals in that the parasite has a complicated life cycle. Eggs from the urine or faeces of infected humans enter watercourses where they hatch and infect various species of snail. After a stage passed in these, minute larvae emerge and swim in the water, being swallowed by Man or piercing the skin when he wades or bathes. Once in the body they develop into flukes which inhabit the blood vessels and produce chronic anaemia, fibrosis and ill health more severe than that of hookworm disease. The greatest misfortune about bilharzia is that it is the *disease of irrigation*. New channels, new tanks and dams for the storage of water in arid areas all harbour the snails by which the disease is transmitted. With it, in Africa, goes a less important but more spectacular parasite, the Guinea worm. The host of this is a minute crustacean (Cyclops) – once the larva has entered the human body from water, it grows and migrates under the skin, forming a boil, which contains about a yard of worm. This must be extracted gradually, for if it breaks the whole thing will become painfully septic.

One whole group of parasites, less internationally important than the 'big three', but unpleasant enough to their victims, can be eliminated by *cooking meat and fish*. Raw fish contains the cysts of a large tapeworm, which can develop in Man into a truly enormous and long-lived parasite. Raw meat likewise can contain cysts of various kinds. Pork, in particular, may contain minute encysted worms (Trichinella) which, when the meat is digested, migrate into the muscles of the eater – especially those of the tongue and diaphragm, causing asphyxia in very severe cases. An outbreak of this disease in Mexborough just after the war was due to the eating of raw sausage meat made from 'measly' pork. Many products such as ham, rollmops, smoked salmon and anchovy are in fact eaten raw – most of these are from forms which do not harbour such parasites, or are inspected during manufacture. Raw flesh is a real enemy, however, especially in countries such as Japan, where raw fish is a popular article of diet.

We cannot here describe all the life cycles of all the important parasites, nor the enormous amount of careful work which has gone into unravelling them. Odder to the biologist is the mechanism by which some of these parasitic patterns have evolved. Why, for example, in the case of the common round-worm (Ascaris) do the larvae which hatch from swallowed eggs enter the blood, migrate through the lungs, up the throat, and down into the intestine again? By what precise mechanism did the worm which causes elephantiasis develop a cycle which brings it into the blood stream only during those hours when its vector mosquito flies? In all such parasitic mechanisms, complicated evolutionary forces must have been at work. Parasites too are selective – only certain snails will act as hosts for bilharzia; only certain mosquitoes are suitable vectors for the malaria parasite. Advantage can be taken of this exclusiveness in breaking the chain of infection. In the case of multi-stage parasites like the tapeworm, which passes one phase as a bladder-like tumour in the muscles or brain of a host, and the next as an adult worm in the intestine of the animal which eats that host, it is important for the human patient which of these phases he harbours: tapeworms in the intestine of Man as final host are injurious, but an echinococcus cyst in the brain of Man as intermediate host is disastrous.

Thanks to these animal parasites alone, Man in say tropical Africa, has for generations in some areas, been permanently sick – one and the same individual may harbour several such diseases: various worm infestations, malaria, trypanosomiasis, bilharzia, elephantiasis and hookworm, to say nothing of amoebic dysentery, caused by a unicellular animal parasite. Add to these the bacterial and related diseases – leprosy, tuberculosis, syphilis and yaws, and the life of Man is understandably 'nasty, brutish and short'.

It will be realized from what has been said, how closely the direct parasitic enemies of Man depend on other creatures, which, while themselves harmless, act as vectors or reservoirs of the parasites, bacteria and viruses which attack human life and health. Bats, dogs and rodents are not directly offensive to Man, yet all three harbour the virus of rabies and can transmit it by their bite; dogs and rats both carry the leptospira of infectious leptospiral jaundice; rats are vectors of plague, food poisoning and scrub typhus. Even the domestic cat can carry a relatively benign disease (cat-scratch fever).

We cannot put down as vectors every animal which carries infections transmissible to Man. Were this so, even the horse, which can give us glanders, and which has tetanus bacilli in its intestine and droppings, would be set down a hazard. The name is best kept either for animals such as the mosquitoes of yellow fever, filariasis or malaria, which actually transmit the diseases (and are the only way in which they can be spread) or creatures like the bilharzia snail which are vital links, though themselves innocuous, in a chain of events ending in human disease.

The problem of public health lies in breaking such chains. It is in this context that the plea for extermination of a species is often made – it has been suggested that we must wipe out the wild game of Africa, because they are the reservoir of cattle sickness, and are easier to control than the tsetse fly, its immediate vector. Now and again such measures are justified – the extermination of anopheles mosquitoes in some malarious areas has been near-complete, and few of us would be disposed to carp at the extermination of rats or lice in the control of plague and typhus. Yet it may be that we are coming to the end of the period in public health where such crude methods are justified. Extermination with general insecticides, such as DDT, is not in fact very effective, for the hardy vectors rapidly acquire resistance, while less-hardy or scarcer species succumb, with serious effects on other forms of life – plants which depend on them for pollination, birds which consume them for food. Modern control programmes are coming to rely on selective extermination, where this is necessary, but to choose for preference control, coupled with biological means of tipping the balance of ecology against the unwanted species. In this field, much remains to be done – we are still over-enthusiastic about indiscriminate chemical war against pests, and have spent too little time on the study of attractants, repellents and natural allies – enemies of our enemies. This emphasis is now rapidly changing. The pest control of the future may look very different from the widespread spraying of today.

This consideration is even more important when we come to deal with the last, and most numerous of the environmental enemies of Man – those which attack not his person but his food supplies. We have incurred the risk of this kind of competition by the invention of agriculture. Food-gathering peoples depend on crops and game which live in a mixed community. One does not find, as a rule, a 'pure stand' of apple trees or bean plants in the wild. By bringing together large numbers of plants, and large herds of animals on restricted range, we lay our food-stores open to the same epidemic or epizootic attacks which occur in crowded human societies, and to a vast expansion in the numbers of pests. Plants and animals have indeed their diseases in the wild, but agriculture makes it easier for these to spread, with consequences which can be economically costly, like the destruction of the vines by Phylloxera aphis, or even socially catastrophic, like the virtual depopulation of Ireland in the 1840's, when potato-blight struck a one-crop economy and starvation followed. The fact that all major cultures are now closely geared to agriculture has meant that Man has given hostages to his environmental competitors, and is more vulnerable to climatic, plant and animal hazards than he would have been if he had stayed in the ecological landscape and merely collected the available food. A food-gathering species is like an investor with a widely spread portfolio – one failure will not put him out of business. A rice or grain or potato economy is far more easily upset.

We cannot, like the food reformers, go back to a 'natural' economy – a 'natural' apple is about as big as a walnut, and 'natural' oats are inedible. What we can do is to extend and develop our knowledge of the inter-relation between organisms, of which both agriculture and parasitism are special cases. This is particularly important when our own numbers are outrunning the available sources of food. Much of the attack on scientific agriculture is ill-based, and reflects a common human bias in favour of obscurantism, back-to-naturism, and sentimentality in dealing with other forms of life. But there is this much truth in that attack, that if we are to import science and operational research into plant and animal husbandry, as we must and should, we need to be certain that it is good science, based in a wide grasp of biology, and planned with foresight rather than improvised. At the moment we may be compelled by profit or food shortage to outrun our powers of anticipating the long-term results of our action. It may pay better, and indeed, be more satisfactory, to mass-rear poultry in batteries than to run them on free range. To do this we may need to protect them against the ill effects of overcrowding by antibiotics. These in turn may produce effects on ourselves, or on other organisms – by spreading drug sensitivity, or increasing the number of resistant organisms, for example. This is a hypothetical example. Experts have foreseen these outcomes, and presumably are on the watch to avoid them. But new knowledge, new substances and new techniques are being applied so rapidly, and in the case of food production, with such urgency, that we can only be sure of avoiding trouble by ensuring that we have a supply of first class biologists, trained in the ecological view of our environment, and by seeing that they are properly consulted before commercial or political factors are allowed to overrule them. It is this kind of planning, not 'back-to-naturism', which is the best insurance against blunders like those which led in the past to the extermination of useful animals, the spread of harmful ones, or the creation of deserts and dust bowls. Man's capacity to interfere with his environment and to attack enemies and competitors has long moved at the pace of a bullock cart; now that it moves at the pace of a racing car it requires equally skilful driving.

Chapter 6

Population, Food and Environment

IT IS only recently that we have stopped regarding an expanding population as the final achievement of human progress – as a species or in a given nation. Biology seemed to side with such a view. After all, fitness in evolutionary terms means one thing only – the ability to produce the greatest number of fertile progeny. The growth of human numbers is direct and tangible evidence of the success of Man. It is only in the present century that that increase, and its own rate of increase, have provided equally tangible evidence that Man has escaped from ordinary evolutionary controls, into a situation which confronts him with a choice: either he must contrive to deal with the problem of his own numbers by the use of his capacity for intelligent social behaviour based on forethought, or the old evolutionary controls upon excessive numbers – disease and starvation – will reassert themselves.

There are indeed what Malthus termed 'natural restraints' on the growth of animal populations – the chief of these being death from starvation, especially among very young individuals; epidemic disease and behavioural changes brought about by high incidence of foetal resorption and of infanticide among the offspring born; while the anxiety of competition due to over-lapping territories can produce death from fighting and even from shock. None of these mechanisms is acceptable to Man in his present frame of mind; least of all infanticide, which is the traditional human method. Yet it is only a few years since a *stable* birth-rate which failed to rise continuously was regarded as evidence of falling national status. Barely fifty years separate anxieties over Britain's impending decline, due to a 'baby shortage', from today, when every responsible biologist would concur with Sir Julian Huxley that 'the problem of growing population is the problem of our age'.

We do not know the size of the population of Early Men – it has been estimated at perhaps half a million in the Lower Palaeolithic, rising to two million in the Upper Palaeolithic, about 25,000 years ago. These densities are based on guesses drawn from the size of modern hunting-tribe populations. For their first 40–50,000 generations men were apparently few – though relatively numerous compared with many other mammalian species. The corresponding population today is about 2·5 billion, and the present rate of increase is about thirty-four million per year, or four thousand per hour.

The most serious feature of this vast increase, from the socio-economic standpoint, is the shape of the curve of growth. Before 6,000 BC the world population can hardly have reached twenty million. It did not reach a hundred million before 500 BC, and did not exceed five hundred million until the end of the seventeenth century: by the mid-eighteenth it reached the one thousand million mark, doubling in about two hundred years: early in the twentieth century it had doubled again, this time in only one hundred years. At present rate it will take sixty years (until about 1980) to double again. This is then a typical exponential curve (one which goes faster the farther it goes in time). If we break down the increase over the last two thousand years and look at it on a logarithmic scale, which enables us to see its structure, it appears that there have been three major spurts in human numbers, coinciding with the three great 'breakthroughs' which we have already described: the advent of tools and cultural transmission, about one million years ago, which set Man on the road to his present phenomenal success: the invention of agriculture, which enabled him to multiply by about three orders of magnitude, or a thousandfold; and the invention of scientific medicine and technology, which brought him where he is now.

The unmanageable character of the present increase is aggravated by the fact that it is not uniform. The population increase due to science and technology was confined to the cultures which developed those achievements, and while rapid, was at least spread over the years which were required for the necessary discoveries to be made. Those discoveries, however,

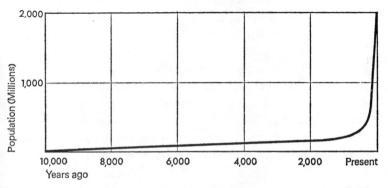

FIG. 6.—The population curve plots the growth of human population from 10,000 years ago to the present.

are now being applied very rapidly to the rest of the world, including those parts which are still demographically in the prescientific period, and over the next century it is virtually certain to be complete. The critical phenomenon is not an increase in human fertility or fecundity – in post-scientific cultures these have if anything tended to fall. It is an increase in child survival.

Pre-technical societies have early death rates, between birth and adulthood, of anything up to fifty per cent, with a correspondingly high young adult death rate, all from preventable causes. It has for thousands of years been necessary, if one wished to ensure the continuance of one's name and descent, to have six or seven children.

A remote collateral relative of mine, Michael Comport of Castle Cooling in Kent, buried all but four of his twelve children. Their graves, side by side in the local churchyard, are described by Dickens in the early pages of *Great Expectations*. This has been the common experience of the human species, in Western and Eastern countries alike.

Different causes operated in different countries. In England, it was diphtheria, scarlet fever, smallpox, measles and the other epidemic diseases which thinned the eighteenth-century family. In Ceylon, until recently, it was malaria. But while in Britain these epidemic causes of child death were gradually controlled over about two centuries, malaria in Ceylon has been virtually abolished in less than half a decade, bringing down the combined death rate for all ages from twenty-two per thousand to twelve per thousand, and the pre-adult death rate vastly more. In England, the birth rate has shrunk if not to keep pace with the change, at least substantially. In Ceylon, however, it has not changed – nor, without special and urgent measures, will it change before *these* extra children reach marrying age. At the present rate the population of Ceylon will double every thirty years.

There is a fundamental difference between *this* breakthrough, in death control, and the more gradual breakthrough of the agricultural revolution, which enabled Man to multiply by providing him with larger and more stable food supplies.

Our initial reaction has been to talk in terms of increasing food production to catch up. If we can feed Britain, then given intelligent planning and the right economic and political institutions, every country except a few with special problems, such as Greenland, can theoretically do the same. This – which I would call the optimistic view – appeals naturally to the humane and equalitarian, and to those who for religious reasons believe that it is sinful to limit the number of our offspring. But as a realistic answer to the problem of exponentially increasing mankind it is, taken alone, wildly unpractical. Of course we must vastly expand food production, and devise means for its sensible distribution, to avoid gluts and waste in one culture and gross starvation in another. But we are not doing this fast enough to feed the people who are now alive. Tristram Shandy took a month to write up each day of his life story, and never got further than his first pair of trousers. We have not yet got a system of world economy, and we do not seem to be within easy reach of one. We are slowly beginning – on a scale which is trifling compared with the energy expended on divisive activities such as the arms race and the feud between rival socio-economic ideologies – to develop new forms of food technology. But the commodity of which we are most short is *time*. If we could exactly feed all the world's *present* population by AD 2000 we should still have considerably more than that population getting nothing, for the estimated number of persons in AD 2000, given present trends, is conservatively put by demographers at 6·267 billion, as against some 2·6 billion today.

There are two conclusions from these facts which we can no longer avoid. One is that we are going to be obliged over the next century, as members of a privileged 'ethnic group', to cut down our own consumption of foodstuffs radically, or prepare to brazen out a period of gross social inequality between haves and have-nots on a basis of 'Hang you, Jack, I'm waterproof'. This is what privileged classes have done before, but it requires no social conscience, only the foresight for lack of which the French aristocracy lost their elegant but unemployed heads, to see that we are *not* waterproof, and that our underfed fellow-men will not starve to provide us with two-pound steaks (which are shortening our lives in any case). Either we shall stick to our fair share, or we shall be made to do so: and since even this will not provide enough to go round, we had better begin thinking hard. This, moreover, applies quite as much to the Marxist as to the capitalist world – Russia and even China are not now chronically underfed, though they have less to waste than America or Britain; they can still greatly expand consumer production of *goods*, but can expect nothing like the same expansion in food production.

The second, irresistible conclusion is that something must reduce the present effective replacement rate. This could be a return of the involuntary infanticide by disease, which is the old pattern of human experience; a sharp rise in deliberate infanticide and abortion, both classical human techniques of limiting increase which are not culturally acceptable to us, but which continue unchecked on a large scale in many places; or alternatively a planned voluntary reduction in the number of children per couple through a change in the cultural attitude towards large families. I suggest that the third of these is, on all counts, the most acceptable. It is also attainable if we do not allow it to be obstructed.

There are three ways of reducing the number of our progeny, other than by killing them or allowing them to die. One is by abstaining from sexual intercourse – thereby renouncing not only reproduction and family life, but one of the least-dispensable parts of ourselves, upon which our social and personal adjustment is built. It is pointless to advocate this, since in any case we are not constitutionally able, as a species, to do so without gross damage to our humanity. The second is to confine sexual intercourse to infertile periods of the month: this is the method of reducing fertility most advocated by the opponents of contraception – it is also the most unreliable, and one which requires as much trouble and instruction as methods of far greater efficiency. About twenty per cent of Indian villagers were able to practice it efficiently after intensive instruction. They were probably the most regular or the least fertile twenty per cent. The third is to devise and make widely available methods of preventing conception except when it is actively desired.

Such methods have been used with varying success by primitive peoples for centuries. It is only in the last fifty years that science and the decline of religio-moral opposition have made reasonably effective contraceptive methods available in a form which can be used by everyone, namely the latex rubber sheath or the combination of a spermicide with a physical barrier (tampon, diaphragm, etc.). Neither of these is ideal. Both can give some measure of effective birth control if consistently used. In India, which alone of the great problem areas is at a relatively early stage in its population explosion, though already facing famine, such methods are being combined with voluntary once-for-all male sterilization. In each case the difficulty is less in the logistics of providing instruction and equipment than in the difficulty of altering a traditional attitude of mind – reinforced at the unconscious level by the ambivalence which we still feel towards infertility.

The urgent need is for a safe, cheap, reliable and harmless non-appliance method, capable of use by illiterates, with only minimal instruction, and without prejudice to sexual pleasure – which is often the only pleasure a deprived community can enjoy; as the song says

> 'If it was nae plenty
> puir folks wadna get it...'

We are on the verge of such a method in the development of hormone preparations which inhibit ovulation – 'the pill' – when taken daily over part of the whole of the menstrual cycle; and we are within striking distance of preparations which can be taken in single doses, either by the man or by the woman. One might hold that for an initial objective we should rather rely, in the interests of *quick* reduction in the size of families, upon developing a safe early abortefacient which could be taken as soon as a period is missed. Male methods all encounter the resistance of masculine pride – which in other cultures even more than our own confuses fertility with virility. It may be necessary to create for such preparations a real or a suggested reputation as heighteners of sexual pleasure and performance before they become widely acceptable. Meanwhile, given active research, and an end to obstruction, effective methods of controlling the rate of population growth without affecting health, subsequent voluntary fertility or national pride – which bitterly and rightly resents attempts by prosperous Westerners to 'cut down the number of natives' – are now within reach. It seems inevitable that they will be developed and used. This is a more than unwelcome expedient, however. It represents the final stage in the process we traced throughout primate development, whereby the reproductive function of sexuality in Man has been gradually separated from its new and highly important social and psychological functions. We are doing no more than complete this process, but in so doing we open up a new human liberty.

A more recent – and even more important – development, by reason of its effectiveness and cheapness, and in spite of certain drawbacks, is the revival of the intra-uterine type of appliance, tried early in the century by Grafenburg. This appears either to prevent embedding or to dislodge the embryo (its exact mode of action is uncertain). The modern plastic loops, bows or rings are easily inserted without an anaesthetic in any woman who has borne a child, and cost only a few pence each. If their promise is justified, the chance of mass use will far outweigh the occasional cases where they become dislodged or produce backache. They come close – by preventing the lodgement of the ovum – to the safe early abortefacient which I suggested earlier in this chapter as a high priority.

All in all, we still know little of human reproduction – relatively far less than we do about the reproduction of animals. The prospects for research are wide and are not confined to population control – we can already promote pregnancy in the infertile, and we may fairly soon be able, if we wish, to influence the sex of offspring – an effect which has so far in human history been producible only by infanticide. Human embryo tissue can be reared in the laboratory (not to produce test-tube babies, but to study the process of normal and abnormal development). One can think of many other, less revolutionary, advances which are on the cards – a sure-fire aphrodisiac to assist the treatment of psychogenic impotence, for example.

The operative phrase is 'if we wish'. One can sympathize with the reaction of those who view biological control over our sexuality with anxiety. Sexual behaviour – as we have seen and shall see – goes far deeper in Man than biologists realize, and there is a risk of using science to act out unconscious fantasies, implicit in the view that if something can be done it should be. If we keep our heads and acquire insight into our unconscious processes, it should not. There is nothing sacred about the technically feasible – it is technically feasible to exterminate Man, and there are abnormal people who appear anxious to do so, assisted by the less-abnormal but technically intoxicated. The proper question, in answer to the pathological mechanizers of behaviour and the equally pathological tremblers before any new freedom (which by definition is 'against nature' or 'contrary to God's will' revealed to them by what they have been taught by others) is 'Do we wish this? Whose liberty or happiness will it increase?' Population control does increase both our sexual and our personal liberty, and is necessary for survival. There are cases where artificial parenthood, the choice of son or daughter, the induction of twinning, the heightening or lowering of sexual response, might each do the same. We need only fear ourselves and our tendency to allow others to dictate to us for the relief of their own inner anxieties, not the techniques themselves. There is no impiety in being able to control our sexual processes at will – only in abusing techniques by forcing or forbidding others to use them. The Church today is not judging the 'pill': the 'pill' is judging the Church, in the light of basic human needs. Biologists, and the use made of their work, will be judged in the same way.

While religious and political dogmas make some people reject the idea of controlling population, I know nobody (except perhaps a few merchants who profit from scarcity) who is against increasing the world's food supply. It could be increased by political reorganization, and probably cannot be increased without political reorganization, but a vast real increase in production, utilization and conservation is needed as well. Applied biology has already worked wonders in this direction (it has been doing so since the first human farmer decided that it was better to grow food as a crop than to hunt for it in the wild, though he did not call it that). The improvement of strains, both plant and animal, by breeding is one of the most important human discoveries after the scientific method, and all the more remarkable for having been done largely by trial and error. If every one of the world's cattle was one half as productive as a pedigree Guernsey, India and Africa would never again have a shortage of dairy produce. Provided that fodder is available this is probably not an unrealizable aim.

There are a few relatively simple ways in which we could increase existing food resources. A visit to India, where many communities have traditionally avoided the killing of animals for food on moral grounds, is likely to awaken a certain amount of conscientious fellow-feeling in any biologist – who respects life occupationally, because he studies it. It will also remind him that whether or not it is moral to eat mammals, it is certainly wasteful to do so. The source of the energy we derive from food (and it is calories which most people lack today, together with first class protein) is the radiant energy of the sun. Plants convert this into carbohydrate and protein – in general, Man gets his carbohydrate direct from the plant, but allows animals to convert plants into milk or meat from which he derives his protein. One reason for doing this is that animal protein is more nearly 'first class' than that derived from most plants, except nuts, soya beans and the like: another is that Man cannot digest cellulose, which is the main carbohydrate ingredient of green plants, whereas cattle keep special bacteria to do so.

The highest efficiency of solar energy conversion into carbon is found in wet lands and forests, tropical and temperate, which are largely inedible by Man. Cultivated vegetation has a lower efficiency, while in any case not all of most food plants can be eaten.

Plants capture about 0·1 per cent of solar energy falling on a given area of ground. Herbivores eating the plants capture about ten per cent of the energy in them, and carnivores about the same fraction of the energy in herbivore flesh. The sun-to-final-energy cycle of herbivore-eating plant and carnivore-eating herbivore is only about 0·001 per cent. Vegetarian diets are accordingly much more efficient in terms of solar energy per square metre of ground than are carnivorous. A shift from animal to plant food would in itself, if it were universal, put up the available food energy tenfold, and we could do better still with any of the theoretically feasible systems which transfer solar into chemical energy directly. The great drawback of all these, however, is the rate at which we need to increase food production to meet population requirements which are now with us or are inevitable whatever we do. New techniques require technicians – to put them into effect on the scale needed to make any serious impression on world food shortages must take time, and time is what we have not got. A realistic crash programme must really rely on techniques *already familiar* to vast numbers of people, such as farming and fishing – techniques which can be brought up to date, but are not basically new.

Special techniques, however, have their place for the future and for special places. At the moment, the use of energy to de-salt water would be one of the most strategically placed special techniques, adding a sizeable arid fraction, much of which has only, like the Sahara, become arid recently, to the available and habitable land.

The shortage of protein (particularly in Africa, where it is difficult to keep livestock efficiently owing to disease and drought) makes it desirable to find ways of obtaining it, either directly, through the culture of bacteria and algae in special solutions, or from ordinary plants, which contain a fair amount if we can get at it.

The first of these techniques is being tried in Israel, which has plenty of solar energy but too little water for stock farming. This scheme is effectively to use algae and bacteria to make protein and carbohydrate from inorganic salts and air (there is also the possibility, once we understand exactly how the plant traps solar energy, of making sugars directly from carbon dioxide and water, dispensing with the plant altogether). The second method, that of extracting protein for emergency use direct from non-food plants such as grass, or troublesome pests like the water-hyacinth, is the basis of Dr N. W. Pirie's 'mechanical cow' at Britain's Rothamstead experimental station. Grass fed into this machine yields a green and rather unpalatable protein material which can nevertheless be made tolerably edible, and could quite possibly be added to bread or milk-substitute in quantities sufficient to keep African children from getting protein-deficiency disease (kwashiokor). The cellulose residue can still be passed on to animals to be processed into meat or milk, or split artificially to yield sugars. The main check on further development – let us be quite frank about it – is that protein deficiency and the feeding of children is less exciting to disturbed gentlemen in office than the discharge of 50-megaton fireworks and the intimidation of their opposite numbers in other countries. That is a matter which only combative public opinion can remedy; fortunately it appears now to be beginning to do so.

Of the sun's energy only a very small part falls on ground which can or could yield vegetable crops, even with irrigation. By far the largest part falls on the sea. This is a region which we are still exploiting exactly as our remote ancestors exploited the primeval forest – by hunting and food-gathering, combined with the intensive killing of 'big game' (in this case whales) which seems likely, in spite of international whaling agreements, to cause their extinction. We no longer hunt sheep – it is wasteful and time consuming; the sheep we can rear are infinitely superior to the wild sort, and provide wool and milk as well as meat. But to a great extent we still hunt fish.

Early human society was transformed by the invention of agriculture – it brought about the change from food-gathering and hunting communities like the Aborigines and the Bushmen to settled communities which could support a large population.

The difference between wild grass-seed and the cereal crop, between the crab-apple and the orchard apple, is the measure of the increase in yield which relatively simple and pre-scientific agriculture produced, even by hit-and-miss methods. It made civilization possible.

The sea covers about two-thirds of the earth's surface and collects a proportionate amount of the sun's energy. It is productive throughout almost all its accessible volume, and even its extremes are probably more fertile than the corresponding extremes on land, if only because organic debris falls, and must settle at the bottom. Our present relationships with this source of food are still only very slightly less primitive than the Bushman's relationship to the land, and unlike the Bushman, who lives near enough to starvation to miss nothing which is accessible and edible, our hunting is highly selective (with the vegetable part of the sea's output we do virtually nothing). Lately, to the alarm of biologists, we have taken to using the sea as a general dumping-ground for radio-active waste.

Compared with the cycle of protein production from solar energy on land, protein production on the surface layers of the sea may well be potentially the more efficient, and require less processing. It has also an enormous agricultural advantage which is not normally found on land – that we need worry much less what species are present in the yield.

It is important for the shepherd to keep a 'pure culture' of sheep, because both grass and wolves are inedible. But although some fish are more palatable than others, and a few are poisonous, it is usually possible to calculate marine protein yields in terms of 'biomass', total weight of fish per unit volume, without much distinction of kinds – or even, in some cases, total mass of organic matter.

The analogy with sheep is false in another way – we have long since ceased to get mutton by the inefficient and chancy method of hunting it. The prize Southdown or Merino is a very different and a more thrifty beast compared with the wild sheep. So is the domestic fish, even when he has not been extensively improved by breeding.

Unlike that of sheep, the growth rate of fish depends directly on food intake, and in many cases there is no effective maximum size. We can see the consequences of this very convenient behaviour in the highly efficient fish-raising economies of the Far East, where freshwater fish of large, edible kinds are kept in the flooded paddies and canals (which they keep free of malaria) growing very fast and producing a constant and practically waste-free source of good protein. The fecundity of fish, moreover, is enormous, so that even slight protection and feeding vastly increase the numbers reaching useful size.

Fisheries research is at present largely concerned with conservation and population statistics – both of great importance – because the relatively concentrated fishing of a few species in a few areas makes control necessary if overfishing is to be avoided. But we shall have to go very much beyond this as our own population growth increases. The first step is obviously to substitute cultivation for hunting and food-gathering.

It is possible, with a certain amount of expense, to fence areas of sea – lochs and fjords in particular – and cultivate fish in them. The experiments at Loch Sween during and after the war showed that in a sea loch of this kind fertilizers dumped directly in the sea returned quite rapidly in added biomass of fish and of fish-food. The control of fish under these domestic conditions has since become much easier with the discovery that their movements can be directed by electric currents, and this technique is already in use both for fishing and for fencing hydroelectric machinery inlets to keep fish out.

Even without special techniques, however, coastal waters could already provide much of the extra protein needed. The chief problem in getting and using it is, as in all such matters, lack of will rather than of potential – will, that is, comparable with the energy devoted to what Dr Pirie rightly calls 'foolish or pernicious research' for various pathological motives.

There are others – perishability is one, palatability and prejudice are others. The biologist can produce more, bigger and more palatable fish, but the community will not gain much unless it is ready to eat them, and to arrange methods of distribution which prevent exploitation and impossible prices. The harvesting of the sea has only begun. Even if breeding of sea fish proves uneconomic, there is a vast potential tuna fishery on India's doorstep. The fish of African coasts and even of the Atlantic are nowhere near fully exploited; only the region easily reached by trawlers from Northern Europe is being over-fished, and even there only certain products of the sea are taken.

Fish caught in bulk must either be preserved by refrigeration, carried alive, or eaten and processed relatively close to the point of catching, and the populations which are shortest of protein live in the hottest parts of the world: they also include a number of peoples who have an ingrained distaste for fish products. Research has already gone a long way to render not only the protein but also the oils from processed fish tasteless; synthetic 'milk' can be made experimentally in this way – the present objective is an inoffensive protein additive which can be included in flours, breads or soups without making them fishy.

There is no reason, too why we should not develop methods of fish-rearing in parts of the sea away from land-based fishing. Fish can be controlled in their movements environmentally or behaviourally as well as electrically. The shepherds of large parts of the world do not fence in their sheep but move with them.

Ideally, for economic purposes, we should cultivate and process plankton – the varied mass of small plants and animals which float at the surface and provide the food for larger forms (the whale lives wholly on them, and grows to a vast size extremely quickly – more so than any other mammal). Or we can take out our supplies further down the food chain, by breeding fish. At the moment the possibility of doing this in the sea is limited, but Asia has a long tradition of fish-breeding in fresh water, and experiments on the rearing of plaice to a less vulnerable size before releasing them into the sea are in progress in Britain with very good results.

Speculative biologists have talked about factory-ships producing plankton 'meadows' in artificial bubble-rafts and keeping flocks of fish under them, herded electrically or by trained dolphins as sheep-dogs; more seriously practical experiments in increasing fish yield by dumping fertilizer in the sea, or boosting replacement of flatfish by rearing them like trout to the size of a coin, so as to avoid early mortality, have actually been carried out.

My picture (Fig. 7) is a pure flight of fancy (it may be nonsense, that is, and nobody knows if such an arrangement would

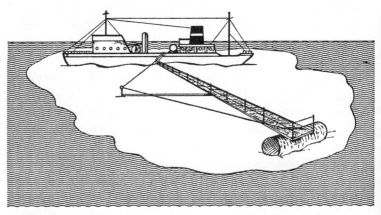

FIG. 7

work), but it shows a factory ship surrounded by a 'float' of artificially stabilized foam containing nitrogen-fixing bacteria and algae, which draws fertilizer from the air and carries a complete ecological food-chain on its underside, the crop being processed on the spot. We could certainly, at least, harvest the plankton of natural sea surfaces, as the whales do.

All these forms of 'mariculture' affect only the upper layers: what could be had lower down we still do not know, though Piccard's bathyscaphe, by reaching the bottom of the Challenger Deep at seven and a half miles, has shown that we can get there if necessary (this, incidentally, is almost as remarkable an achievement as the sputnik: its originator has succeeded in getting government backing, after years of propaganda, solely because the sea bottom has become militarily important).

'What we need', said an American authority, 'is to breed a sea-going pig.' For the same expenditure on research that gave us the sputniks, we could probably multiply the food potential of the sea tenfold. There are difficulties as already mentioned – not all peoples will eat fish, and the transport of fresh fish in tropical countries is difficult. But it was difficult to make a sputnik-carrying rocket.

A world which made full use of biology for useful and humane purposes would be a remarkable and interesting place. Ethics apart, it might be less concerned to eat animals than to use their natural behaviour to serve us – we do not eat sheep-dogs, or carrier pigeons, and there are innumerable other examples of animal behaviour which could be turned to human advantage. Some botanists already train monkeys to collect plants or pick coconuts; since whales and dolphins have been found to be highly intelligent we might co-operate with them rather than exterminate them to make margarine.

Biological control of pests by their natural enemies is a direct extension of the process whereby for instance, birds control locusts and caterpillars. It has been said that if it were not for one species, the drongo, there are places in India where no crops would survive the insect pests. We are already using tape recordings of bird calls to control bird behaviour, the odour of the king-snake to repel other snakes, of lion to repel dogs and foxes, and of fox to repel rodents. Examples of this type of behavioural control ('non-violent biology' in Professor Haldane's words) could be very much extended. They appeal both to our good nature and to our good sense.

I am making no special philosophical pretensions for biology when I say that it presupposes an attitude of mind which should really be general in science, but which more mechanical branches sometimes lose sight of. There is a real affinity between this kind of non-violence which is not sentimental towards animals but enjoys understanding and observing them, and an attitude which finds more satisfaction in feeding humanity than in frightening, threatening or exterminating it.

This, too, has an important bearing on another aspect of population – the risk that before we are mentally prepared to control the process, Man and fully domesticated animals and plants may be the only inhabitants of a planet completely covered with human artefacts. It is not, I think, mere sentiment to recoil from this idea. A world wholly devoted either to housing or to feeding Man would be both intolerable – as over-urbanized countries are rapidly becoming intolerable: it would also be biologically vulnerable. One of the great drawbacks of massive over-population is the harm it does to the human environment through air and water pollution, extermination of animals and plants, creation of dust-bowls, and haphazard urban development destroying natural resources. Apart from the aesthetic damage it does and the social problems it brings, such overgrowth is dangerous because inherently unplannable: we shall have exterminated whales before we know what whales could have done for us; and so on. In other words, if we let our hand be forced by over-population and over-urbanization, we shall find we have lost wealth and opportunities, as well as basic satisfactions, which we can never replace. I shall come back to the importance of some of these in a later chapter.

Chapter 7

Ageing

ONE of the most characteristic features of Man is that he has a fixed life-span. We know from skulls that Pekin Man very seldom managed to survive beyond middle life – yet very early in the growth of human civilization it must have become known that however robust or cunning a warrior might be, and however he might avoid or propitiate the hazards of his environment, the days of Man are three score and ten, or at most four score: in other words, between the seventieth and eightieth year of life, strength declines, disease multiplies, the rate of deterioration steepens, and for all but a very few life comes to an end. Now and then a man may reach the century, but such individuals are rare. We may die at any time then, but even on the most optimistic estimate we can name a date when we shall almost certainly be dead. Much of our social planning – life assurance, for example – depends on this fixity of life span, this certainty of eventual decline. It has played a still bigger part in human thought – not only does death come to all eventually, but we know roughly when it is likely to come – more so now than in any previous age, because we have eliminated, to a large extent, the causes of premature dying which prevented most of our ancestors from reaching late middle life.

The effect, present in Man and in many, but not all, other

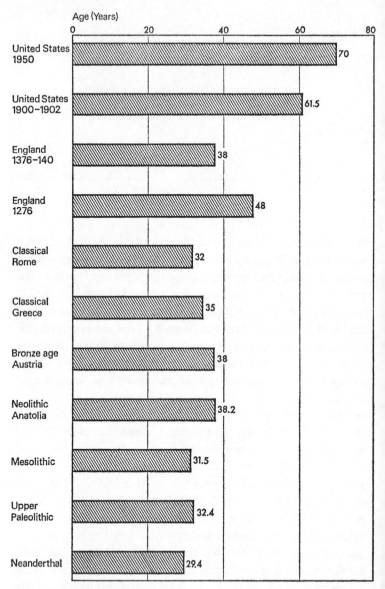

FIG. 8.—Chart showing longevity in ancient and modern times.

animals, which causes vigour to decline in this way with time is called ageing. We can make a very rough estimate of its progress in a given individual by such indices as the decline in muscular strength, the whitening of the hair, the wrinkling of the skin, and the loss of energy and well-being, but these vary a great deal between persons: what we effectively measure when we measure ageing as a whole is the *increase in the liability to die*. The only way to measure this in an individual man or animal is to measure the stress or injury necessary to kill him: for practical purposes, then, ageing is something which, in spite of its profound effect on the individual, we always measure on a population, and its most direct measure is the probability of death during the next unit interval of time. In a prosperous modern society, a man of seventy is about three times as likely to die during his next year as a man of thirty, and about fifty times as likely as a boy of ten. If we kept throughout life the same rate of mortality we had at the age of ten, we should die off at a constant rate of about 1·06 per thousand per year, and we should have a constant 'half-life' of several hundred years; such a population would decline like a population of radio-isotope atoms, and would have no typical life-span. Such ageless populations do occur in the wild, among small birds and mammals. In these there is no ageing as we see it in Man, because the standing mortality at all ages is so high that it masks the decline in vigour at the end of life. These creatures do not age because they do not live long enough to do so. Chaffinches in the wild have an annual mortality over fifty per cent, but a chaffinch in a cage has lived twenty-six years. Under good conditions in captivity they have a survival curve very like that of Man, with a period of infant mortality, a period of adult vigour, and then a decline of the population to zero through a steady rise in mortality with age. This pattern appears to be general in mammals and birds – it used to be thought that cold-blooded animals, capable of continual growth, might be genuinely ageless, in the sense of having a constant mortality regardless of age, but recent work has shown that fish age very much as do mammals, albeit, in the bigger kinds, more slowly. It is not certain whether reptiles and amphibia do the same (they are so long-lived that direct experiment is almost impossible) but it seems likely. In fact, the only animals which are genuinely non-ageing are creatures such as the sea anemone, which replaces all its cells continually, and is more a culture than an organism.

Ageing is an unpopular process with Man – it means that at the height of his status, experience, and skill he gradually finds his strength and health leaving him, until death or invalidism force him out of business. It is a depressing prospect – more so than that of sudden death at an unforeseeable age. Accordingly throughout history one of the favourite human fantasies has been that of getting the better of age. There were legends of physical immortality, and magical ways of getting it. The goddess Aurora prayed for immortality for her mortal lover Tithonus but forgot to pray for eternal youth – Tithonus accordingly lived on and on, becoming more and more senile and decrepit; until he prayed for death. We shall have reason to come back to Tithonus in a modern context. Meanwhile there have always been ingenious men who were not satisfied with fantasy, and were convinced that given time and knowledge it might prove possible for Man to get control of his life-span and control, or even reverse, the process of age-deterioration. The sexual mysticism of the Indian temple-builders, the researches of the alchemists, and much philosophical speculation, were all devoted to this aim. By the end of the nineteenth century such enthusiasts had lost heart. There was a brief flare-up of interest following Brown-Séquard's and Claude Bernard's work on the sex hormones: Voronoff grafted chimpanzee testes into men, and Eugen Steinach operated on the testicles, in the hope of producing rejuvenation. But none of this work came to anything, and the subject fell into disrepute again. Books were written to prove that ageing was 'inherent' and mystically proof against human interference (this has been a common intellectual response in past ages too – if we cannot alter something unpleasant, we will call it 'inherent' and treat it with reverence).

Over the last ten years the whole picture has been changed, however, with the emergence of a new interest in gerontology, the study of the fundamental control of age processes. With the disappearance from prosperous countries of the killing diseases of early life, the sharpness of the age decline in vigour has become more and more obvious. It used to be thought that if only we could control all individual diseases, one by one, the human life-span could be pushed up to 100–120 or more. This has proved a fallacy. The chief characteristic of human ageing is that although one organ may be harder hit than another, there is a general increase in the vulnerability of the whole; cure one disease and another appears. From the changes in the shape of the curve of survival with improved medical knowledge, it seems clear that while in time we might by this means get practically everyone through adulthood to the seventies, nearly all will still be dead by the age of ninety. Improved medicine, moreover, can postpone death without increasing vigour or preventing physical and mental decline, and we have found ourselves producing Tithonuses – kept alive by medicine, but not able to enjoy the extra time given to them.

For this reason, biologists all over the world have turned to investigate whether or not it is likely to be possible to interfere, not with single diseases, but with the timing-mechanism of human ageing as a whole. This research has so far produced no far-reaching results, but it is early days yet. This is quite a different aim from that of general medicine. General medicine tends to make the survival curve squarer and squarer, as more people reach the typical death-age for the species. Gerontology aims to push the entire curve to the right, to increase the longevity of the species by actually slowing down ageing. Whether it will prove possible to do this, how large a change we may hope to produce, and by what means we might produce it are still not known, but with six hundred teams clocking on daily in the USA alone to work on problems connected with ageing, and growing activity in other countries, results should soon appear.*

Among the animal species which have been studied in this growing investigation, there is an apparent association between ageing and the possession of non-renewable cells; the few forms which do not appear to age are from groups in which all the body cells appear to be renewable, while at the other extreme those lower animals which cannot renew any body cells at all (nematode worms, for example) age very sharply.

Vertebrates and higher animals generally, including ourselves, contain both renewable cells (skin, blood or intestinal lining cells, for example) and non-renewable cells which, once formed, remain with their possessor for life – brain cells, striped muscle fibres and others. We also have structures which are not renewable, though their individual cells are: we can grow new kidney tubule cells, but if a whole tubule is blocked or damaged by disease, our kidneys will be permanently short of that tubule – we can heal wounds of a finger involving the replacement of many cells, but not grow a new finger.

Research today on the main mechanism of ageing in Man (there may be more than one mechanism, of course) is largely based on three alternative hypotheses. The first of these is that ageing involves the loss or deterioration of those cells which we cannot replace – either through random injury, or as a result of such fixed cells having a 'built-in' life-span after which they die or cease to work properly.

It is certainly true that the numbers of some of these irreplaceable cells which are countable, notably brain cells and muscle cells, falls with increasing age. A cell may, moreover, be failing to function normally without actually disappearing or showing any obvious change to our rather insensitive methods of observation. If loss of irreplaceables does in fact 'time' human

* In the years 1958, 1959 and 1960 the US Department of Health spent sums of $4·5 million, $7·7 million and $12·4 million on research projects in the field of age studies, and this budget is still increasing. The attack on the human life-span has moved out of the field of science fiction into the field of practical politics.

ageing, we have only moved the problem back one stage; it would then be a matter of asking why non-dividing cells age. All our cells are subject to slow damage to the chemical 'instructions' contained in their chromosomes, through the process known as mutation. Presumably the stored instructions in the nuclei of non-dividing cells are being impaired in this way, as well as by chemical side-reactions in the cell; if this sort of damage to fixed cells is the 'clock' which times ageing, however, it must run at different speeds in different animals – mouse and human cells are not very different, but the cells of mouse brain are only required to live for a maximum of three years, while those of Man may have to survive in sufficient numbers up to and beyond a hundred years. One of the problems of investigating such hypotheses is that it is very hard to study mutation in non-dividing cells, and even to count them accurately. That such cells have a built-in life-span seems to be borne out by the results of experiments in which, in inbred strains of mice, tissues from old animals have been implanted in young hosts but failed to live longer than the donors from which they were taken.

The second hypothesis is that ageing may be due to changes in successive generations of those cells which are renewed – in particular, changes of the kind which are described as 'faulty copying'. If we make a negative by photographing a photograph, print that negative and photograph the new photograph, and so on, the successive copies will be of lower and lower quality. It may be that a similar effect operates to make successive generations of new cells less and less effective, so that the new cells produced by an old man are in some way less viable than the new cells produced by him when he was a child.

Here again, much interest has focused on the possible effects of body-cell mutation. While mutations in a fixed, non-dividing cell may eventually kill it, mutations in dividing cells, unless they kill, or prevent further division, are passed on to that cell's progeny. A killing mutation is likely to be unimportant for ageing, since a replaceable cell, when it dies, is replaced. If, however, through mutation, it were to be replaced with a cell which was chemically different, inferior in some respect, or actively harmful the co-ordination and 'programme' of the body would be progressively upset. It is precisely this kind of gradual drift into instability which we see in the ageing mammal.

In favour of 'faulty copying' as causes of ageing, it is argued that we know mutation does take place in body cells, and they must therefore become more diverse during life, except insofar as mechanisms exist to weed out any which are too far substandard. One group of harmful mutations is already known – that which appears to produce cancers of different kinds – and these, as we know to our cost, the body cannot weed out. There might be others – one possibility is that mutation in the cells which produce antibodies, the lymphocytes, might break down the barrier which exists against the production of antibodies to one's own body constituents, and set up immunological civil war. Or mutated tissue cells might be inactive without being replaced, as they would be if they died. Normally, if we were to lose half our liver cells, new cells would be produced to replace them, and our liver would grow back to its old size, but no bigger. Clearly some balance-mechanism must control this. If, however, half our liver cells had stopped performing some essential function as a result of mutation, the body might not recognize them as 'gone' and the stimulus which replaces lost liver cells might not act; if half my employees die, I shall know it and engage others – if half of them attend but do no work I may not know it until my business goes bankrupt. It is even possible that a few mutated liver cells might produce substances causing the body to inhibit the activity of normal liver tissue; if a crooked manager draws the salaries of a hundred imaginary employees, I may be stimulated to sack a hundred real ones to keep my staff constant, and find I have nobody to work for me.

All these views of the possible effects of faulty copying in ageing are entirely speculative. They have come to the fore at present for one reason only – the widespread research interest in radiation. We know that radiation is one cause of mutation in body cells. It has also been observed that in mice, exposure to very low doses of x- or gamma-rays or neutrons reduces the life-span in proportion to the dose, and that this life-shortening has some of the appearances of accelerated ageing. Accordingly much experimental and theoretical energy has gone into the attempt to ascertain if, and how, the radiation-induced shortening of life represents a speed-up of the normal age changes, whether it only mimics them, or whether it is something wholly different. This question cannot yet be answered with confidence. It may still be that ageing is timed in Man by mutation in a particular group of dividing cells, causing them to change in character and activity. It seems more likely that if mutation is an important factor, it is in non-dividing and irreplaceable cells that most of its important effects occur. We are likely to have the answer to this question over the next few years. It has been discussed at length here, because this particular answer could well be our first important breakthrough to the understanding of timing mechanisms in human ageing. One minor speculation which could be practically important is that *if*, as is by no means certain, the mechanism of cell-injury in radiation damage and in natural ageing is the same, drugs developed to protect against radiation damage might conceivably have effects on life-span. Experiments on these lines have been conducted already, but without conclusive result.

The third current line of investigation concerns not cells but molecules. Much of the structural matter of the tissues consists of fibres which are composed of large colloid molecules, and in some of these, especially the substance collagen, steady changes are known to occur with time. Such changes are attributed to chemical side-reactions and to what is called 'cross-linking', the formation of chemical bridges by which molecular properties are altered. Age changes in collagen and elastin are apparently responsible for the loss of elasticity in senile skin – at the same time, such colloid changes have relevance to the other chief hypotheses, which depend on mutation or information-loss in cells; the information-carrying molecules of DNA are themselves colloids and fibres, and some workers rate deterioration of this kind in the instruction-store and the working parts of a non-dividing cell as more important possible causes of age deterioration than mutation in individual genes. Here again, time will tell – it does not look as if any large part of human age deterioration is due primarily to changes in structural molecules such as collagen; information-carrying molecules are another question.

So much for the main lines under investigation in gerontology at the present time. It is a measure of the rate of progress in them that five or ten years ago, the chief current hypotheses would have been different and far less experimentally verifiable; at the same time, in including them in a book such as this, there is not overmuch risk that they will be out of date within another five years – though within ten we should be able to choose between, or reject, them.

It should be noticed here that few serious gerontologists now look to hormones as the answer to human ageing. Changes in hormone production occur with age, and hormones can be of value medically in its palliation, but it now looks as if the timing of age changes does not lie in the declining activity of any one endocrine gland – the 'growth' hormone of the pituitary gland, which plays a part in maintaining the chemical attributes characteristic of young tissues, and the anabolic steroids, which may affect muscular strength, probably undergo age-determined changes, but few workers now believe these to be primary.

One might well add at this point that there is no known rejuvenatory nostrum or régime which effectively prolongs human life – of those advertized directly, or more effectively through rumour that an unrecognized genius is rejuvenating a Pope or a President, some are fraudulent, others, like Voronoff's chimpanzee testicles, could never have worked for fundamental reasons unknown to their inventor; others, like Steinach's operation on the testis, or Dr Aslan's use of H3 (novocain) probably have some physiological effects but are certainly not agents of rejuvenation. With the growth of scientific gerontology, public credulity on these matters may temporarily increase. No such treatment has ever referred to the only real index of ageing or its postponement, the survival curve. They have all depended on subjective improvement in strength, morale and especially sexual performance. But these are precisely the things which are most easily improved by suggestion. Even the age-wise loss of potency which so often drives patients to the 'rejuvenator' is typically a psychological, not an inherent physical change. Suggestion is a mode of treatment – who shall say that the patient who goes home happier, temporarily more potent, and feeling that somebody is concerned for him, is not rejuvenated – except the coldblooded actuarial statistician, who shows that he lives no longer than might have been expected if he had not spent a fortune on 'tissue extracts', Royal jelly, and the like?

The point is that such treatments achieve no better results by expensive and irrational methods than a good modern geriatric unit can achieve by rational. They do not alter the natural life-span, though they may cheer a few ageing subjects and make them think themselves younger. Any ageing person who wants to benefit from modern knowledge will do far better consulting his doctor, or a geriatric unit, than with an unorthodox 'genius' who promises him magical results. The aim of the operational attack on ageing, by contrast, is to discover its chief timekeeping mechanisms so that we can fundamentally alter its rate.

Whether in fact this will prove possible will depend on what the timekeeping mechanisms turn out to be. That it may be so is strongly suggested by the fact that in at least one mammalian instance a large gain in life-span can be produced by the simple expedient of restricting diet – rats and mice treated in this way can be kept artificially young for periods equal to their normal life expectation. This might not prove an appropriate method for Man, whose growth pattern is quite different, but it indicates that in some mammals at least the timing mechanism is accessible. We have suggested another possible access route in mentioning the attempt to find drugs which protect fixed cells against deterioration. Wholesale replacement of aged cells by grafting, while it may become technically possible in the relatively near future, and serviceable in cases where one organ is notably more damaged than others, is hardly an answer to ageing, since it seems unlikely that *all* the deteriorated tissues could be replaced, and brain-cell loss could hardly be made good in this way, at least if the personal identity of the subject was to be retained (this is a nice philosophical point – a more practical one is that although some organs may lead, the body ages as a whole, and subtotal renewal by grafts is likely to be chiefly palliative).

While research on the eventual control of ageing continues, the effect of general medical and social progress on the survival curve, which became most evident in Europe during the last two hundred years, is now spreading rapidly to Asia and Africa. We saw from Fig. 6 that this effect is a squaring of the curve, the ends remaining pegged – that more and more people, in other words, are living to reach old age and die at the so-called 'specific age' for Man, between seventy and ninety. While from very early history a few individuals have always reached these ages, now the majority of people in Western countries do so, and the majority of people in the world eventually will. This change has nothing to do with any eventual change, due to fundamental interference with the rate of ageing, in the specific age itself – it depends simply on the application of medical, social and industrial techniques already known and fully worked out in the developed countries of the world. The first part of this gain is the biggest; the simple application of, for example, vaccination in China or improved child care in India can double the percentage of children reaching adulthood, and consequently the number of candidates for eventual old age. Each successive increment after that becomes harder to secure, and in very prosperous and advanced countries the squareness of the curve is reaching its realizable limit.

There has been a good deal of anxious writing about the effects of medicine in increasing the percentage of aged people in the population, and of the dangers of fundamental inter-ference with the life-span, if this became possible, in an over-populated world. These are based largely on a misconception. The proportion of older people in civilized countries is rising as a result of medicine. In the US the total population over sixty-five has risen from three million in 1900 to nine million in 1940 and 12·3 million in 1950 – the forecast for 1975, assuming present birth and mortality rates, is 20·7 million out of an expected total population of 221 million – rather higher than the present 15·7 million out of 177 million. The fact that a high proportion of this over-sixty-five group will be non-working is not wholly an effect of ageing; it is also largely an effect of the social pattern in our culture which fails to enable fit older citizens to work as long or as usefully as they could do. The really grave difficulties inherent in this growing older popula-tion nearly all spring from defects in our attitude toward it. At the same time, since ageing is a loss of vigour, in all senses, an older population will contain an increasing number of dis-abled or infirm people. By far the biggest rise in the non-working population over the next century, however, is likely to be in the proportion of children to adults. Taking US figures again, it is now some 67 million out of 117 million, and is expected to rise by 1975 to 85 million out of 221 million. In point of fact, the length of dependency in early life is also increasing through the far longer period of education and training which a technological society requires. Nobody in Britain now goes to work to support himself at thirteen or fourteen, and few of the skilled technicians of the future, farmers or engineers, will be fully productive and experienced before twenty-five, even if they have begun to contribute to produc-tivity by that age. The rise in 'passengers' is therefore due to three factors – more elderly people, without a corresponding change in social pattern enabling them to be fully productive; more elderly people who, though infirm, are kept alive without regaining their health, Tithonus-fashion; and a longer period of pre-adulthood due to higher educational demands, with a corresponding reduction in fully productive life. Some of this is offset by the increased individual productivity which these individuals will have in a technological society, but the fact remains that a producer will not reach his full potential until he has spent nearly fifty per cent of his life-span and fifty-five per cent of his working life, if we retire him at sixty-five, or if he becomes infirm at seventy.

The answer to this problem is quite clearly not to stop work on the fundamental biology of ageing and to concentrate on Tithonus-production. The aim of this work is not to increase the period of infirm old age, but to increase the period of adult vigour. At the moment, in farming, which, as the basic source of food production, is the key industry to meet world population needs, and in which there is no compulsory retirement, full productivity is not reached much under twenty-five, while experience goes on growing throughout life; at the height of this experience, however, age and death cut short the life of the farmer. If it were possible to increase the period of adult vigour by only the modest amount of five or ten years, so that a man of sixty retained the vigour which he now has at fifty-five or at fifty, without any corresponding increase either in child-hood or in the period of senile infirmity, the result would be an enormous recruitment in effective production. So far from producing 'passengers' in society, a breakthrough in this field would reduce the proportion of each life spent in dependence, and the reduction would fall in the years where usefulness is maximal and wastage due to ageing is greatest. Next to the control of excessive fertility, work to bring about this increase in individual useful life is quite the highest priority in solving the problem of food, because there is little chance that sophisticated methods of food production can come to replace traditional agriculture fast enough to meet the needs of those already born. The effects on productivity of ordinary public health measures against, for example, malaria and hook-worm in increasing food production are already striking illustra-tions of this. These measures increase fitness and survival in early adult life, but when China, Egypt and other developing countries approach the survival curves now seen in Europe, the effect will be exhausted, and only a fundamental interference with the length of adult vigour can produce another comparable gain.

We have only lately begun to make a proper study of the patterns of ageing in industry and society, but two things are already plain – that continued interest, work and usefulness within the individual's capacities are a preservative of health and vigour, especially mental vigour: and that we are not providing sensibly for the change which medicine has already brought about in human survival. It is traditional in modern industry to dismiss the most experienced men – this is the implication of compulsory retirement. The assumption behind it is twofold – that beyond the age of sixty-five many occupations become too heavy for men who, in the nature of things, must be expected to ail more than their juniors; and that older men are lacking in judgment and initiative. Both these assumptions may have some truth in them, though we negative the second by retaining such figures as judges and politicians far into manifest senility. Neither assumption is wholly true. What is undoubtedly true, however, is that pending a breakthrough in the actual control of ageing – which will not come very soon, and may prove beyond our reach after all – *one of the most important public health needs in modern urban societies is a radical revision of our attitude towards the employment and social position of the old.*

What form this should take has yet to be worked out, with due regard to many non-medical factors, such as trade union fears of 'dilution', employers' fears of damage to the promotion structure, and the loss of status involved when a senior man continues to be employed after retirement in a different capacity from that in which he rose to the top. It has also been very difficult so far to find proper facts about the performance of ageing men in different occupations, about their numbers and health, and about the measures needed to better their position.

In Britain twenty per cent of men employed in any industry will have changed, or be about to change their job by the time they reach their mid-sixties; by seventy, another twenty per cent will have become physically unable to work at all. Figures differ in different occupations, survival being greatest in farm workers, chiefly – and this is highly instructive – because for them the choice of available activities is greatest; very old men can mind sheep or feed poultry. In most occupations only forty to fifty per cent of the labour force is still in the same trade at sixty-five. 'Light 'work is often sought, but investigation shows that in this context lightness has a special meaning – a change to work which, although sometimes physically harder, is not time-stressed. At the same time, even in heavy occupations, ten per cent of British dockers and fourteen per cent of engineer's labourers work into their seventies. The limiting factor is not muscular – the old hand may have the knack of lifting loads which a younger man cannot manage – but the ability to work without being hurried.

Causes of accidents likewise differ; young men are injured because, through lack of experience, they do dangerous things – old men because, in doing things they have long learned to be safe, their strength or balance fails them.

If retirement is a matter of social custom, non-industrial roles are even more so. Our grandmothers were old ladies at forty because they were expected to be so – today women of seventy may dress and act like their daughters, and perform the same social roles. Even the decline in sexual interest so long assumed to be a natural part of the ageing process seems itself to be the product of social expectation. At the same time, the stream flows in both directions. Social expectation can keep us young, but the need to compete with younger people, if it is compulsive, can upset and stress older people as much as time-stressed work. We need a society in which age-roles are optional – in which the individual can choose his or her own, without pressure either to withdraw or to participate, and in which each of us can find esteem, security and continued interest in conditions tailored to our physical and mental capacities as these change.

Chapter 8

Man as His Own Enemy - The Future of Human Nature

'HELL', said a Sartre character, 'is other people.' It can also be ourselves. Man is the only animal which is inherently able, corporately and individually, to be his own worst enemy. That groups should fight each other, a phenomenon very rare in other animals, and probably confined to social insects such as ants, is a side-effect of the change from biological to social evolution. We no longer behave as a single species – individual societies may by contrast behave as if they were competing species within one habitat and prey on each other; even, in the case of some cannibals, for food purposes. Were this all, the liberal optimists who have long hoped to abolish aggressive behaviour by making us politically One World would be on sound ground. Unfortunately there are other forms of human hostility which reflect not real competition but the ability of the human individual to be in deadly conflict with himself.

Self-injury and even suicide are not unknown in animals. They take the form of self-mutilation in stress situations, and occasionally reflect human-looking emotions – as in survivor of a pair who dies of self-starvation on losing a mate.

Man may injure himself as an individual, and men may injure each other. That we should group together 'human follies' at the individual level – alcoholism, suicide, smoking cancer-producing cigarettes or breaking one's neck mountaineering – human follies which assail others – war, crime, murder, selling

145

poisonous foodstuffs, dangerous drivers, etcetera – and diseases, which are 'nobody's fault', as all being manifestations of a self-destructive capacity in Man is a relatively new idea – one which would not have appealed to our eighteenth-century ancestor, but one with which the human biologist, whose interest reaches out beyond factual matters such as blood groups and genes to human behaviour as a whole, must now begin to reckon.

The most straightforward, but least fully investigated, examples of disease from human interaction are the so-called 'stress diseases'. We have to be cautious in attaching this label – new ailments appearing in a society, if not infectious or due to some other obvious cause, are liable to be put down to stress or to the tempo of life. Probably the most important stress of this kind at present is the high rate of change. There is also argument between schools of psychology over the mental elements which make a situation stressful – simple inconsistency in the demands made on one can produce stress, to judge from dog experiments, and physiological psychologists emphasize these elements, while psychoanalysts emphasize inner conflicts and the need to repress emotions and wishes as the main stressful factor. Both are occupationally interested parties, as are biologists and sociologists, but both are probably right.

Psychosis – frank 'lunacy', that is – is a similar problem; it is certainly determined by the forces which determine our other reactions, but there is a sameness about its manifestations in widely different people which suggests that the final state, (depression, schizophrenia in variety, dementia) is in part a physical reaction. It seems to call for a two-pronged attack, partly by way of its content and family origins, and partly by way of the peculiarity in the individual, genetic, mental or acquired, which makes him respond to childhood and later stresses by *this* disorganization rather than another – factors like those which determine that one of us breaks down via asthma, another via migraine, ulcers, or bowel disease and a third not at all. The mental versus physical causation argument is often a reflection of the researcher's own view of life, but we can praise God who makes His scientific creatures of various forms, for it is not yet clear at what point in the sequence we can most profitably intervene to relieve the disorder; even to the student of whole people, it is a relief when a major problem is open to physical palliation by medicines, even if that is not the whole story.

Gastric ulcer is one of the most popular candidates for the title of stress disease – it is a condition associated with urban living, sedentary work and responsibility. Which of these, if any, can be said to *cause* the condition ('precipitate' would be a more scientific word – what causes tuberculosis?) is not known. The facts we have are chiefly based on disjointed observations – ulcers are commoner in executives than in lower clerical grades, and in London omnibus drivers than in conductors (who have to run up and down the stairs of the double-decked vehicles several hundred times a day). At the Walter Reed Institute in America, ulcers have been produced in monkeys by making them take stress-loaded decisions. The 'executive' monkey would receive a small electric shock if he failed to press a lever periodically – at least once in twenty seconds. Such monkeys rarely let their attention wander enough to receive a warning shock, but they died of ulcers. This looks more like a product of forced attention than of 'executive' decision, but deaths became more numerous and ulcers more acute in onset if the monkey was subjected to alternate sessions when it need not press the key, and test-sessions (marked by a red light coming on) when it must. After twenty-three hours of this régime the unfortunate monkeys collapsed with acute ulceration of the stomach.

Urban man in the so-called 'ulcer belt' will have sympathy with them; he must watch the lights to avoid being knocked down or given a ticket, his change to avoid being gypped, his neighbour to avoid being outdone, his potency in case it flags, his body-odour in case he has one and his leaders to avoid being bombed to hell and back. But is this really more stress-producing than the insecurities to which the Aborigine or the

Neanderthaler was exposed, or the insecurity of the Indian villager living between famine and the moneylender, with small-pox thrown in? And if it is, in what particular? Survey studies showed, oddly enough, that the level of 'anxiety' and of 'neuro-ticism' measured by tests was *higher* in India than in Britain and the US – but this clearly depends on the investigators' definitions of anxiety and neurosis. Possibly Indians are more willing to feel and admit unpleasant mental sensations than the Western executive, who likes to look busy and stressed (to prove his efficiency) but not to look anxious (which implies he is falling down on his job) and who might be fired if he burst into tears. That might suggest that ulcers are a feature of the 'stiff upper lip' belt – whether they are commoner in the old boys of English public (private) schools than in plebeians of com-parable social standing does not seem to have been scored. (The scorers did not even specify whether their Indians were urban or rural.)

That quite specific conditions, rather than general free-floating stress, may be needed to produce specific ill effects is indicated by the monkey experiments: stepping up the propor-tion of time during which key-pressing was needed, and shortening the rest-intervals, did not cause ulcers – the six hours on, six hours off schedule did. This could be related to the findings of Pavlov, the great Russian experimental psychologist, and of numerous later workers that uncertainty is a great disturber of behaviour. If a dog is conditioned to expect food when he sees a circle and a shock when he sees an ellipse, and if the circle is then made steadily more egg-shaped and the ellipse more circular, the point is reached at which the animal cracks up and refuses to play at all, becoming instead bad-tempered and sickly. As a matter of fact, it could be argued that uncer-tainty is greater in our society than stress, because of two factors – the very high rate of change within one lifetime which makes the world of each generation very much different from that of the last; and the quite unique combination of social mobility and individual diversity. Genetic polymorphism occurs in all societies, but cultural polymorphism is a feature of big cities and big nations. All Samoans are not identical in behaviour and belief; neither were all Sioux or all Aztecs. But because of differences of culture, custom, attitude and upbringing, Samoan and Sioux personalities would be quite different – one would admire what the other despised, and be ashamed of what the other would be proud to do. Deviant people in each culture would probably have fitted better into the other, but the pressure of social conformity would keep all but the very deviant within the culture. Our society is much more like a mixture of Samoans and Sioux, and all the other tribal patterns. There *are* cultural unities which make us all Americans or all Englishmen, but our upbringing may range from tyrannical to permissive, our norm of behaviour from aggression to submission. Most of us it is true, are near the middle of the distribution for most characters, but still with a big diversity. At the same time, even in childhood, we have much more choice forced on us than is ever found in a small homogeneous tribal society. We may be born into Jewish, Hutterite, atheist, Quaker or Catholic homes, and if so are likely to stay with the group, but we have the choice, and many people reject such early training and join another group – often with conflict. We may be born poor but become rich or born into a seafaring community and become attorneys or bank clerks. Such changes may be due to choice, accident, or unconscious compulsions of our own, but they all embody the potentiality of choosing what we will do, and the conflicts that involves.

The old Scots poet said that

> 'Freedom is a lovesome thing,
> Freedom makes man to have liking'

but it is possible that freedom forced upon us also makes Man – who evolved in the tight, primate social context of the small one-track society – to have gastric ulcers and anxiety states. Such subtler conflicts may play more part in making us uneasy than do gross evils such as wars, pestilences and famines. War

149

even integrates us by making us temporarily, and often undesirably a one-track community and a happy band of brothers, united only in the desire to down the enemy, but nonetheless united. Cynics have suggested that scientists should conspire to fake a threatening invasion from Mars to make men unite against the imaginary enemy and so solve their problems of diversity. The devil once fulfilled this role, and the bogey of the 'other', which we considered in dealing with race hatred, may indeed serve at times to shield us from anxiety and diversity. But it is a big price to pay. It is said that the public health campaign in Communist China never got so well under way as when the public suspected that the diseases and pests they were urged to eradicate had been put there deliberately by the American Government. We might get rid of famine and inequality in the world if we were convinced likewise that the Communists or the Martians, or even Satan, had organized it out of spite. One problem of civilized society is to find a peg on which to hang our frustrations without the political and intellectual consequences of blaming them on malicious enemies. Another is to find a way of accepting rapid change without being confused and rendered sick by it. Possibly the difference between anxiety caused by starvation, disease and the like, and that caused by (or associated with) our present prosperity is in the degree to which present fears, real or not, trigger off deeper and more destructive sources of inner mischief. What is clear is that *mere* stress – from climbing Everest, or even from being in a concentration camp, while it can harm us, does not do so in quite this way. War, with the risk of being killed, even reduces the incidence of some anxiety-manifestations (its chief associated anxiety in our culture is the fear of being seen to be afraid). Outer conflict seems to reduce our capacity for inner conflict. Man has used it in this way, both within and between societies. Since it has now become prohibitively dangerous, that bolthole is closed. Ulcers may therefore be quite genuinely a part of the price of civilization.

We should look further at this, because, oddly enough,

medicine itself may be complicating the picture by *curing* us of ulcers, or of other ailments. These conditions are 'self-destructive' in the long, or even the short term, but every doctor knows that illness is a refuge from tension. At a recent psychiatric conference a young physician had just finished a paper describing the skin diseases, headaches and indigestion he had successfully removed, when an older psychiatrist rose to ask him if he could really sleep soundly after depriving so many people of their only support in life. This is a hard saying. However, we have inner tensions which are common to humanity – we cannot express them in hate at home, or society will founder; we cannot express them by hating collectively, or we shall soon exterminate Man – and if we express them by going sick, we shall be operated on and our ulcer cut out. This could be the obverse of primate evolution up to the twentieth-century stage – *we are being individually expected to be 'reasonable' beyond our capacity*, 'reason' being the non-expression of troublesome emotions. Failing other outlets we may turn to alcohol – which is the growing problem in prosperous neutral countries with good medical services! Fortunately primate and human behaviour provide an answer to this dilemma, but we should examine the problem more fully before prescribing remedies.

It seems to be universally agreed by primatologists that healthy wild primates almost *never* fight within the species; even the strict dominance we see in some species is established by a kind of behavioural consent, not by violence. But primates confined or stressed do exhibit the kind of aggression, often pointless, which we see in human hooligans, politicians and delinquents (I am not being sarcastic). Either Man differs in this respect from all other primates, or aggressive and destructive behaviour is a sign of stress, of one kind or another, in him too.

Both alternatives are probably correct. Some cultures have valued and inculcated pugnacity, just as there are in some places whole tribes who are professional thieves. In these, what began as a special situation has become a fixed and learned response, handed down from father to son through the attitude of the community. But in cultures which, like ours, disallow violence in daily life, outbreaks of it, whether they are expressed in wars, riots, or breaking up public property, *are* symptomatic of stress. If the affluent societies have hooligans, those hooligans are cases, not of primate original sin, but of stresses, unobvious to the rest of us, perhaps, producing a disorder of behaviour. Outward-turned aggression which violates our cultural rules is a stress disorder, just as much as inward-turned aggression expressed as suicide, self-frustration, or illness. It is easy to guess at the nature of the stresses (most observers simply produce any feature of contemporary life of which they personally happen to disapprove) but the human biologist has a sizeable task ahead in finding out exactly which of them are the most important in producing these untoward effects.

Man and subhuman primates are both capable of 'inner conflicts', but Man is very much the more so. Like other primates he is also able to externalize such conflicts in irrational behaviour (what in lower animals is called 'displacement activity' – an inappropriate piece of behaviour which relieves tension when more appropriate responses are blocked). This, at the individual level, can presumably lead to self-destruction in both Man and animals if carried far enough – only in Man, however, is it expressed socially in behaviour which could destroy the species.

Irrational behaviour actually plays a far greater part in Man than in other social primates which have been studied, since so much primate behaviour is neither 'rational' nor 'irrational' but socio-automatic. It is this large slice of socio-automatic behaviour in Man which is liable to a take-over by unconscious forces which render it not intellectually neutral, as in apes, but actively irrational, because in conflict with our conscious wishes.

The question of instincts in Man is thorny, and the attempt to identify them probably pointless, if we mean by instincts pieces of complex behaviour which serve a function but are not learned. Man has pseudo-instincts (both normal and abnormal sexual impulses have the compulsive quality for him that instinct has for lower animals) but these are rather complicated derivatives of early experience, and it is probably better to talk in vaguer terms, of 'drives' identifiable in human conduct, leaving aside the question of how far they are innate.

The two relevant human instinctual drives have been called erotic and anterotic – we might do better with 'constructive' and 'destructive', for they have come a long way from their original subprimate contexts of sex and fighting respectively. Both have played a large and positive part in evolution: even the apparently unadaptive capacity to turn one's aggression on oneself, which is particularly well-developed in Man, may have positive value, for psychoanalytic evidence suggests that it provides the material of *conscience*, or some of that material. Conscience is a phenomenon we see to some extent in all intelligent social animals (it is well-developed in dogs, living socially with Man at least, and possibly in the wild) but it is most evident in higher primates and Man. The constructive or socializing erotic drive apparently converts even aggression into an extra force for sociality. If the constructive energy is insufficient conscience itself can be a destructive drive in its own right; in our type of society, which lacks some of the supportive mechanisms of simpler cultures, conscience and guilt can be pathologically overactive (not over real evils, but irrationally and compulsively, over matters where there is no reasonable ground for guilt or shame) with consequent illness. Depression and self-destruction, whether by suicide or otherwise, often reflect an overactive and irrational sense of guilt (how far triggered by, or triggering, constitutional biochemical processes we do not know), and the psychiatrist may have the difficult task of making his patient *less* conscientious and more realistic. Conscience, indeed, is always largely irrational, even when it is supporting reasonable moral judgments, and is not a very reliable guide to ethics if judgment and conscious self-mastery can be substituted – conscience, after all, made inquisitors and self-mutilating ascetics as well as saints.

The two kinds of human behaviour which most injure and endanger the species are both manifestations of the destructive drive, and are really one. Individual outbursts of violence are perhaps the most primitive and least serious – they acquire far greater seriousness when they become systematized in society, so that hate is directed against a group of 'enemies' (many of them invested with the characters of some hate-figure out of our childhood). Such enemies may be really threatening or not – in either case irrational aggression is a poor way of dealing with them – and the whole trend acquires momentum by drawing on other residues of infancy, and of subprimate life – dominance-behaviour, which may make us pick pathologically aggressive leaders because they 'look big' and talk big; childhood sexual fears; and the strong human tendency to stuff a dummy which can then be attacked. Where we have pointed to irrational behaviour over such things as race, all these primate, post-primate and human unconscious mechanisms are in play. We can see the whole spectrum, and the magnitude of the past and present risks, in the situation where large sections of the world, armed with nuclear weapons, came to hate each other on principle and out of conscience, and to give at least a partial hearing to even more disturbed individuals willing to exterminate the whole race, also on principle. This danger grows with civilization, for we become less and less ready to express hate against individual fellows, and more and more technically equipped to kill other groups. Either we project such hate into our surroundings 'loose', when it soon settles on someone – the Jews, the Communists, the Negroes, criminals, heretics, teenagers, deviationists or what you will; or we actually swallow our enemy, as lovers wish to 'eat each other up', by another process drawn from primate infancy, namely identification – this process enables us to 'build' our parents into ourselves during early development, but it can serve hate as well as love, and usually does so. A civilized man will sooner injure a hated rival by 'identifying' with him and killing *himself* than by an attack on the object of his hate. Our convention of desperation is suicide, while that of some other cultures is murder (of the real enemy) or, where the enemy is some childhood hate-figure not really accessible to attack, going berserk and killing *somebody*. The aggressive function of suicide is widespread and conscious both in our society and elsewhere. It is the final human way of securing revenge and making an enemy lose face.

From the evolutionary viewpoint, the most dangerously maladaptive pattern of expressing a 'death instinct', or a destructive drive, is that in which it takes over and energizes society itself, dominance-behaviour, politics and the worthiest of evolved moral behaviours – loyalty, love of one's neighbour, hard work and the like – for wholly irrational objects. We are familiar enough with this pattern, and while in past generations it has made human history miserable, in this generation by reason of our vastly increased destructive powers we must end it, or it will end us. We may have begun to acquire biological psychoanalytic insight into it just in time. Individual self-destruction may look less important, but it depends on exactly the same forces, expressed piecemeal, and its medical and social significance is vast. We each potentially contain our own Doomsday Machine, and share the derangement of the individuals who wish to make such a machine in fact. It is with the individual expression of the death 'wish' that psychiatry is often concerned, and from the standpoint of human biology we may as well begin there.

A surprisingly large amount of human behaviour which looks accidental or random has turned out to be purposive at an unconscious level.

Indeed, in quite a high proportion of cases where people injure themselves, they do so 'deliberately', albeit quite or almost without conscious intention – whether the injury be by reckless actions, alcohol, social mischief such as quarrelling or crime, or even, one suspects, actual organic disease. Every physician sees cases where he may suspect, though he cannot prove, that a torchlight procession of accidents or fully organic ailments has unconscious origins; and the procession is often halted by a change in life situation or a successful course of psychotherapy. It is an alarming prospect that we can harbour such devils, even if their obscure aim is less to injure us than to injure some other member of our internal fauna – the 'introjected' or built-in image of a parent or brother, for example, whom for reasons of conscience we may not attack more directly.

Whether manifested against our fellows or ourselves, Freud saw in these alarmingly destructive tendencies evidence of a death instinct – a biologically curious phenomenon if true. Others have seen in hate no more than the frustration or withdrawal of love, and since aggression, even self-destructive aggression, is a fairly common primate response to frustration, and one which is quite intelligible, the large amount of repressed hate in Man may be no more than the obverse of his capacity for love, arising from his extensive psychological use of sexuality. Another possible cause is the prolonged and dependent infancy, much longer than that of other primates, in which, though apparently possessing feelings just as intense and unbiddable as any young primate, the infant human first cannot, and later dare not, express aggression against his parents for fear of losing their love. Melanie Klein has shown, by ingenious study of adults and of babies, that the infant may really 'fear' that his rage will destroy the mother he needs, not merely make her withdraw until he is better-tempered – in other words, he has the capacity to do little harm, but the biting and fighting response appropriate to a young baboon, coupled with a strong biological drive to remain within and dependent on the family. How this explosive mixture fits into primate development we do not know, but it looks like another process where the behaviours of the ape and the growth-pattern of Man have fallen out of step, with important psychological results, among them the love-hate capacity which has played so large a part in shaping, as well as endangering, human society.

Much of this active life of love and hatred, even in adults, is lived at the unconscious level – that is to say that though the individual is aware of strong emotions or impulses arising from it, he has no conception of what is going on underneath, and may be frightened, elated or surprised by his own behaviour. Societies and social patterns channel some of these impulses (into war, power, delinquency, or public aggression, or into sociality and mutual aid) and private relations receive others – we may love our wife or beat her, without knowing why – but both are relatively insightless, and the coherent patterns underneath are all part of a 'dream time' which has its own, but an unreasonable, logic autonomous from our conscious purposes. It has taken psychoanalysis to get at this, and to expose the part played by infantile guilt, fear and anxiety in setting the patterns of adult behaviour.

A great many other human behaviours, whether they are old primate phenomena like dominance, or apparently rational pieces of the old Adam-like acquisitiveness, and even laudable activities like science, literature or religious devotion, all serve or are used by, our unconscious motives. We do not know if apes have an unconscious, or, for that matter, a discrete 'conscious' mind which thinks along logical lines – they can be logical and illogical like us, at different levels. But the human situation, in which, as it were, directives and messages come to the Head Office from a clandestine department that the staff do not realize is there, with its own logic, its own aims and the solidified inner attitudes of a child of three, must be unique. More unexpected still, and for that reason more impressive, is the fact that Man, so equipped or handicapped, has been able to use the processes of his own mind to uncover themselves, with the ultimate possibility of controlling them. Our problem is to live with our unconscious processes, without letting them control us – we cannot 'get rid' of them (this has been the traditional post-primate and human expedient – to deny and repress such forces; it is probably the need to deny and repress in this way which has split our mind down the middle, and given our infantile selves so much and such dangerous autonomy). If indeed we did 'get rid' of them we should become, like the cat in the physiology experiments, decerebrate – deprived of a working brain (into which they are built) and of all desire, motivation, inspiration, or mental activity recognizably human, for it is our unbiddable half which is the powerhouse for all such matters. This is the human dilemma in the primate series, to find means whereby rationality can take control of behaviour without repression and without losing social or mental energy.

The problem of controlling our behaviour, then, is largely the problem of managing our feelings, our irrational fears and our anxieties, without denying either them or our reason.

Darwin saw the solution in the evolving social nature of Man, Freud in the imparting of insight, which involves at once an intellectual and an emotional experience. Lectures, which can inform us, cannot change us, for they lack this second component. Analysis and depth psychology, though often effective, are still rudimentary and endlessly time-consuming to effect a revolution in our behaviour; there are those unable or unwilling to benefit from them, and the field of insight they confer may be very circumscribed. Ernest Jones points with regret to the irrational religious, political and other opinions expressed in unguarded moments by analyzed analysts, who, in the therapeutic situation, would be the first to recognize them as reaction-formations.

Insight must be otherwise imparted. In fact it must be imparted through society, which is the vehicle of our social and emotional life, together with an equally important controller of our behaviour, support from others. Freud neglected society in his concern at the clinical level with the individual, or saw it – as we have been obliged to see it – as the stage on which summated individual irrationalities are acted out. So it is, but as we are all social as well as irrational, it is also the sum of our social impulses, the moral phenomenon which Darwin held it to be, and which for the Aborigine it undoubtedly is. The traditional 'old' human manner of securing this cohesive insight, tempered with irrationalities according to the culture, is through the group of corporate activities we now call 'religion'. We must be as guarded, however, with this word as we have been with normality, equality, race and the other emotive words we have encountered; for the Aborigine it would mean something very different, had he such a word, from the 'religion' of our eighteenth-century ancestor. He would mean not a system of dogmatic belief and morals, but rather the act of cementing culture and reconciling our impulses to it through a shared series of emotional experiences. More correctly, what we call the religious, ritual, or cult life of the Aborigine is a far wider matter than the 'religion' we hear preached or attacked in our own society. For him it involves a whole battery of activities and concepts which are insight-giving and support-giving without being factual – though at its edges the stories and the dances merge into the communication of knowledge or of techniques. It represents the activities of the 'dream time', and its methods are those of the dream carried into daily life and dramatized by dancing, stories, adornment, careful non-purposive ritual, expiatory and apotropic ('averting') activities directed against built-in fears and dangers, positive affirmations of hopes and joys, and – very important – the discharge of unacceptable impulses of hatred or love through special 'rituals of release'. This is what the psychiatrist calls 'abreaction'. A man who is repressing his fear of battle may get nightmares, and be relieved of them by being allowed to experience panic, and express it, under the influence of a light anaesthetic. More complicated anxieties may be more difficult to bring to expression and discharge, but often some kind of outburst of emotion, not normally acceptable to a culture like ours, which values the 'stiff upper lip', is needed to ventilate them. What the psychiatrist attempts to do in private, primitive Man often does through a socially accepted mechanism.

Actual 'release' rituals vary greatly in technique and content from culture to culture. Some are highly stylized and decorous, achieving their effects indirectly: in the typical 'release' favoured by primitive people, however, consciousness is actually clouded, and the participants are temporarily 'beside themselves'

– restrained from self-injury or breach of the rules laid down by the culture for such occasions by the corporate nature of the dance, the circle, or the observance, or by the presence of a 'therapist' in the person of the priest or master of ceremonies who leads the crescendo of enthusiasm but stands sufficiently outside it to control its consequences and, in time, arrange an orderly subsidence. Drugs, intoxication by smoke and the like have no special advantages, it appears, over more widespread techniques of suggestion in disordering the senses and encouraging the participants to 'let go' – noise, rhythm, forced breathing in unison, rotation (either in a circle dance or by spinning, or being spun, round and round to the point of giddiness). In performances of this kind men become ecstatic and sometimes completely hypnotized – women appear, from film records, to experience repeated orgasms (this peculiarity of the female, to experience orgasm easily by simple suggestion, may explain some features of the sex-distribution of such rites in anthropology). There are excellent films in existence of 'release' rites in progress – among the Pocomaniac sect in the West Indies, for instance: response to 'beat' music is a more familiar but quite typical example, complete with rhythmic noise, exponent leaders, and spontaneous orgasm – we even see an abortive attempt now and then to dismember a sacrificial victim, on more primitive lines still.

This use of religion is not confined to primitives or to tribal cultures. There are elements of it in Hinduism, which more than any other systematized religion treats the unacceptable forces in Man by facing rather than denying them or denying life – its gods have both benign and terrific aspects, as every figure in our lives from our parents on has had benign and hate-inspiring aspects, and as our minds have. Even more intriguing to us, since we know less of them, are the psychodramas or 'exhibitions' at the Eleusinian Mysteries in ancient Greece. Not the least striking feature of these was that in the most intellectually sceptical culture of its time, educated Greeks were so deeply affected by these ceremonies that nobody broke the vow of secrecy imposed on the initiates. They resembled the effects of successful psychoanalysis in that the process was enlightening and at the same time an emotional experience. The very little we do know about what went on there suggests an atmospheric excursion into the 'dream time' in which the elements of the old primate sexual anxieties concerning the reproductive organs were in some way involved, as they so often are involved in the analytic experience – but this experience was also supportive and social, like a primitive ceremony, rather than interpersonal, like the confessional or the depth-psychology session.

It might be wiser to say little about Eleusis, since we do not know what went on there; it seems to have offered promise of an after-life (Diogenes, with his usual scepticism, protested against the morality of a religion which promised a better time in heaven to an initiated burglar than to the just Epaminondas, who was never initiated at Eleusis). The cult was originally that of the corn goddess, taken over by the Athenians, and of her daughter Persephone's visit to the nether world, but this was only the framework for rites which involved, as their critical emotional point, a 'beholding', and the handling of sacred objects. In this sense they must have been very close to the spirit of aboriginal ceremony. 'One can scarcely speak of any-thing so definite as doctrine in connection with Eleusis. The root idea was more akin to magic.'[9]

We could, of course, be on quite the wrong track – the 'draw' of Eleusis, like that of Christianity, may have been simply the promise of factual immortality or a sense of the unreality of death: the telesterium, or temple, was an open-plan building, which could hardly have housed the masonic-type rites, including a 'journey of the soul', which some authors have suggested. Psychodrama of some kind it almost certainly did house, however, and of a kind which struck a chord even in the most sceptical of a nation of religious sceptics.

It looks to us now as if much of the intellectual vigour of ancient Athens was due to the admirable balance struck in its culture between the high valuation it placed on reason and the recognition of the Unconscious as a force to be reckoned with. The Greeks were the inventors of rationalism, and they combined it with a morality summarized in the motto 'nothing in excess' – not even duty, courage or virtue. To such an ideology the orgy as a means of dealing with the irrational in Man might seem highly inimical: and, indeed, the irruption into Greek city society – or rather, the recrudescence there, for they represented a return to old-style nature-worship – of the cults of Dionysus and the Mother Goddess seems to have been highly disturbing. Dionysus was the god of wine, riot and the unbridled release of the 'dream time'. His followers, chiefly women, the maenads, danced wildly on the mountains in a state of ecstasy induced by music, wine, sexual licence and the eating of raw flesh. In the *Bacchae* of Euripides we see respectable women, from the Queen down, caught up in this old matriarchal and revivalist cult, to the scandal of the rationalist King Pentheus. Excess is bad – this conduct is un-Greek and unbeautiful, as well as dangerous and inconvenient. The god must be put down. But the prison which holds him explodes like an overcharged wineskin, while the unhappy King is torn to pieces by his own mother, who brings home his head, thinking she has killed a lion. Without realizing it, Pentheus too has fallen victim to hybris, excess – he has been excessively rational, he has attempted to banish the Unconscious, but the Unconscious, violent and dangerous as it looks to public order, is a God, and cannot be put down.

The Greek solution was unique and typical. Dionysus was invited into his rightful place among the Olympian gods, as the equal and twin of Apollo, the god of rational inspiration and patron of the arts and sciences. His frenzied and licenced maenads became the chorus of Greek Tragedy (the word means 'goat song') in which the audience sees the destruction of heroes through excess, not of wickedness or stupidity, but of virtue, reason, or duty. We do not derive any disquiet from the destruction of a villain, because we do not identify with him. But the destruction of a man through the very conscious ideals we attempt to cultivate strikes a chill, the chill of 'pity and terror' lest we too are overtaken by events we cannot control, and we do reverence to the god of 'dream time', Dionysus, whose altar stands on the stage and whose rites these are. Afterwards we are restored to health by seeing his other face, that of the mocker of reason and good order, when in the following comedy ('revel song') actors in comic masks, wearing huge leather phalluses, make game of all respectability, political, sexual or religious, and play buffoon jokes on solid citizens, the heads of state, the gods, and even their patron Dionysus himself, who is depicted as a drunk, a coward and a layabout.

This transmutation of the orgy into stylized art is another uniquely Greek solution. How far it is applicable to our conditions is another matter. All the violence of tragedy is in the mind, in the verse – none might be shown realistically on the stage. Our art today goes to the other extreme. All the violence is enacted, whether in popular or prestige entertainment. In this respect we are closer to the Romans, a society which never came to terms with Dionysus; compared with Athens its outlook seems to us now limited, smug and uninspiring – its virtues was seriousness (*severitas*) carried to idiot lengths (one must if necessary condemn one's son to death unblinking) and punctuated by the Hitleresque cruelties of emperors such as Caligula and Domitian, who were probably mad, but were undoubtedly popular, and of the arena. Roman drama included the enactment of Metro-Goldwyn-Mayer battle epics in which real human beings really killed one another, or a condemned criminal disguised as King Pentheus was torn to pieces in fact, 'before your very eyes', or, as we should say, for kicks. There are times when instead of complaining of fictional violence we should be devoutly grateful to Dionysus for ketchup and the film camera. The atomic bomb and the Nazi camps could well have been Roman inventions. We would do much better to be Greeks if we can. The equally arid religion of rational-unreason which grew up in ascetic and dogmatic Christianity, with its rejection of joy and rationalism alike, is part of the long-term price civilization has paid for the victory of the Roman over the Greek view of life. It is time to reverse that process and return to Dionysus, under the escort and protection of Apollo, the god of the conscious intellect and of insight.

'Release' rituals have rarely come in pure culture. The orgiast 'works himself up' to attain not only release but rain, fertility or good hunting. Even periods which have accepted such rituals enthusiastically have been inclined to dilute them, as pure abreaction, by using them for purposes involving yes-no factual assumptions – such as the belief that without human ritual activity the seasons will stop. Orgies which belong wholly to the 'dream time' are the perquisite of very simple, pre-agricultural, or of very sophisticated peoples. In Neolithic and Bronze Age times religion was apparently heavily weighted with calendar-customs and calendar-magic, generated by the new interest in agriculture, which made the seasons something associated with human effort, rather than with external forces. These early agricultural societies appear to have favoured mother-goddess worship, and goddesses are closely associated with the other great releaser of emotion, sexuality. With few exceptions, sexual intercourse is the only common experience in our own self-conscious culture in which, if we are lucky, we can get outside our skin as fully as an aboriginal orgiast. We as yet make no social or therapeutic use of it, though, as with L.S.D., some psychiatrists would like to if they dared.

Goddess-worship looks with favour on orgiastic rituals of release, often with a mixture of permissivity and ferocity very typical of the free-wheeling unconscious; patriarchy more often tends to be prohibitive and sexually restrictive, both for Freudian reasons and, possibly, because clearer recognition or assertion of the man's part in reproduction made it important for the father to be identified beyond doubt (there is usually no dispute as to who is who's mother). Our attitude to 'release' rituals stems heavily from the patriarchal tradition as derived from Judaeism. The Bible is a chronicle of the battle between a heavily restrictive paternal monotheism and the more orgiastic cults of other Mediterranean agricultural peoples who worshipped gods and goddesses of the crops and the calendar and, in the view of the nomad puritans who eventually defeated them, 'committed whoredom under every green tree'. In contrast to the Jews, these peoples usually settled under patriarchy for a mixed pantheon, as did the Greeks. Dionysus became associated with the original Earth-goddess Demeter (Earth Mother) and shared with the Triple Artemis and with Demeter's daughter Persephone, Queen of the Shades, much of the old mother-goddess's dominion over the 'dream time'. We can see compromise cults of this kind under similar circumstances in some African religions, which reconcile patriarchal practice with older matriarchy, and the woman's strong hold over the unconscious as the natural story-teller to children. In Hinduism, likewise, Lord Siva is *ardhanarishvara* (half-male, half-female) and can be worshipped as male Intellect, female Energy or both – the most orgiastic cults being those of his left-hand, female half.

It could be argued that we have no good 'release' rituals because we look down on goddesses, or that we look down on goddesses because we fear the Unconscious, or both. The association of the 'mother-goddess' with orgiastic release is not surprising: she can confer not only the satisfaction of forbidden male incest wishes from our infant and primate background, but also the blissful repose of the womb and the full breast which both sexes enjoy, and which 'release' may be attempting to regain – mothers are our earliest comforters and wish-fulfillers, as the baby monkeys reared with angular or cuddly mother-dummies abundantly demonstrate. Mother-sects, however much put down as irrational and disorderly by patriarchal society – for whom, as for some of us, women are 'irrational' and 'disturbing' by contrast with the intellectual and restrained male of the public school tradition – have had great vitality, whether in the worship of Cybele, Demeter and Isis with orgiastic rites or of the Blessed Virgin without. Some modern 'witch' cults are a self-conscious attempt to revive them; in

Hinduism they are quite at home, though unpopular with the respectably Westernized. Patriarchalism, like the public school system, is based on a fear of woman and of the unconscious – this distaste has been reinforced, as it was for King Pentheus, by the fact that quite apart from incest anxieties, 'release' rituals can, among other things, release alarming aggression. The mother who presides in such matters can be the gentle provider, but she can also be the 'castrating' mother of our old infant anxieties, whose sexuality actively threatens us, and from whom patriarchalism is a refuge: human and animal slaughter by the maenads, self-mutilation by the priests of Cybele, and Thuggism in Bengal a century ago were manifestations of goddess-worship as typical as gentler and more beneficent forms of 'releasing' licence. The doubts of Pentheus and Dr Kurt Hahn, the cleanliness of Islam and the educational theory of 'cold baths and codswallop' are equally typical defensive male reactions against the fear of sexuality and aggression in ourselves; the quarantine imposed by blessedness and virginity does not quite still these doubts in patriarchally inclined Protestants; goddesses are potentially disgusting and dangerous, and not even self-castration through enforced celibacy can quite disinfect them. Though we no longer need share the 'Englishman's instinctive sympathy' for the manliness of Islam against the equivocal complexities of Hinduism which Lord Macaulay expressed (we can see its origins too well), all this has to be reckoned with in sorting out the biology of these behaviours for therapeutic purposes. Release of the unconscious *in toto*, whether by drugs, orgiastic ritual, or too much whiskey, can have socially inacceptable consequences even for the modern therapist or 'beat' guitarist, who would not despise sexuality, but has no desire to be torn to pieces and eaten by his patients save at a harmlessly figurative level. Yet it is precisely this dangerous material which Man in general, and our society in particular, needs to find means of accepting and discharging in a harmless form. We begin to see what a striking achievement Greek tragedy or the bloodless Hindu cults have succeeded in bringing off. We, for our part, have not gained much by out-of-hand rejection; paternalism has a cruelty and aggressiveness all its own, and tends to run into the arms of the disorder and self-castration it so much fears – the stiff upper lip and the disgust of the colonial Englishman in India did not make him behave any less savagely in putting down the Sepoy rising than a fitting recognition of the divinity of Kali would have done. One could argue that it might be less savage to dismember and eat an occasional person for the good of society than to kill some millions with gas chambers or nuclear weapons. With a little intelligent thought we might find it culturally unnecessary to do either.

Our 'release' experiences are commonly individual and most commonly sexual. We do not stylize sexual ecstasy after the manner of the ecstatic sects, but our mythology provides for one analogous experience. In the Hindu Sakta sexual ritual it is held to be essential that the parties are not 'involved' (*pasu*: ensnared) – they come together as god and goddess, not as two affectionate individuals, or not only as that. Hence in some of these rituals the partner is chosen at random. She who by reason of ecstasy falls in love with her ritual partner has not attained release – it is the ecstasy (Siva) with whom she should be in love, not a mortal (albeit in private life a wife is the best and most appropriate ritual partner). In ecstatic practice therefore, anonymity and promiscuity are the rule rather than the exception. The domestic sacrament is something super-added to domesticity.

Our mythology allows for an unpersonal love, which is close to the spirit of religion or creativity because it is wholly cere-monial, wholly unpersonal. This is the love one (usually male) feels, and may enact, for and with a woman before one knows her well, when she is not a person so much as a body and a voice. It is, in fact, the version condemned by Christianity as mere lust – it is admittedly dangerous – indeed, it is one of the chief sources of sexual and emotional risk that under unconscious pressures this kind of response is possible and difficult to control – but also uniquely moving, though not in the same way as the tenderness to a known person which makes up married love, or personal love in general. The experience is not so much love as a devotional act by the male towards Woman or Aphrodite – a homage to a 'dark power', not a form of human relationship, at any rate in its inception; and yet it is a communication, and one which can completely and unpredictably re-programme the participants. If revolutions are the locomotives of history, such orgiastic experiences, whether they lead to personal love or not, can be the locomotives of emotional development for those who take part in them; and, as with revolution, the progress can be towards heaven, hell, or most commonly both. The goddess, like all goddesses worth the name, is actually a part of ourselves.

The Tantriks were apparently in some doubt at times how far a real and personalized woman is eligible as initiatrix – one could be initiated in a dream, by a dream-woman. Another peculiarity of this kind of mysticism was that the ecstatic sensation, for the male, had to be divorced from orgasm – nominally because of the need to 'conserve' the magical power of the semen. It looks more as if one object of this avoidance was originally the pursuit of a more generalized, female-type response – not the externalized male sensation localized in the glans – as part of an attempt to 'become' oneself female, to be both Siva and Sakti, i.e. bisexual. The rituals of similar Vishnu sects were less rigorous and stylized about this, but equally concerned with the same point and equally promiscuous. These celebrate the union of Devotion (Radha) with Krishna, the spirit of Play, the Fickle but Constant: it is his power to command the devotion of every woman and be hers alone, though he is many, while before him every man is as a woman (i.e. he commands the boundless devotion of both sexes). This looks like another recognition of a bisexual element in ecstasy. Freud remarks somewhere that there are four parties to every sexual act (man, woman, man-in-woman and woman-in-man) the unconscious having the contrasexual colour. The more unworldly yogis made sex a wholly internal exercise by mentally

168

assuming all these roles – this way, however, was considered appropriate to mystic athletes rather than to 'men of action' (*vira*) for whom the orgiastic rituals cater, or the 'ensnared' common man who observes the conventions and has ritual intercourse with his wife on prescribed days of the month, with the appropriate prayers and observations.

It is noticeable that these ritual ideas are all male-orientated. This may merely be a matter of culture, but in this tradition woman is naturally and by right a goddess. She initiates the man; she requires no initiation, because her capacity for ecstatic dissociation is built in and needs only to be evoked. In our own culture one never ceases to marvel – if one is lucky enough to experience it – at her capacity to heal without verbalizing anything, simply through affectionate contact. This is her medium – in Lévi-Strauss' phrase she *is* communication, as in the Tantrik tradition she is Energy or Empathy, while Man is ideation and concreteness. According to Devereux,[10] in many 'primitive societies' coition 'is much more…than an outlet for passion and affection. It is also the primitive's equivalent of the theatre, the concert, the novel, the Sunday comics, the TV show and the Saturday evening binge…' This, in his view, is a degradation of sexuality to the level of a bromide – Aldous Huxley might well have agreed with him. But it is an effective bromide, and the arguments do not all run one way.

Another quasi-religious expedient of many cultures, and of individuals in all cultures, has been the attempt to produce a particular state or states of mind, variously described, but having at root a peculiar and deeply reassuring feeling of insight plus identity with other men, with 'reality' or with the natural order. This is the common experience of mystics, who have relied to achieve it upon means which suggest that it depends upon activating some train of events in the brain – indeed the same order of sensation occurs spontaneously in some brain disorders; fasting, overbreathing, hypnosis, monotonous stimuli and the like are common recipes for producing it, and some cultures have induced it reliably and as a social ritual by the use of deliriant or 'psychotropic' drugs. The attractions of such an expedient are obvious, if it really offered a short cut to the result obtained, in tribal religious life, only by devoting most of the tribe's time to the performance of rites, or in psychiatry by years of analysis. The Eleusinian Mysteries had the great advantage, in a complex civilization, of being 'one shot' treatments, where the 'patients' returned only for a boosting dose. If 'mystical' experiences induced either by drugs or by rites could really socialize us and dispel the anxieties which disrupt our abilities, and could do so on a sure-fire basis, they would be like successful analysis, only much less time-consuming. The dangers are obvious – addiction to the source of enlightenment, whether spiritual or from a bottle, is only one; a more serious drawback, for our culture, is that the emotional experience, however beneficial, also conveys a disabling sense of intellectual conviction which is proof against argument. Psychoanalysis can do this, but should not if well-terminated; the Eleusinian Mysteries did not convince the philosophers who attended them that Dionysus was a historical person, or that they had a private and non-rational short-cut to the ordering of affairs. Impressive as the effects of the mystical experience may be in dispelling anxiety and making us One, we cannot afford it at this stage of our evolution if the comfort it gives is to be achieved *at the expense* of self-criticism.

We need a word to distinguish this type of religion – the kind which is a device for producing insight-giving emotional experiences which have social effects – from the religion of larger-scale cultures, which is a thin dilution of this with belief, cosmology, legend, history and morals. 'Primitive' and 'tribal' are both inaccurate names for it (nobody would call the Eleusinian Mysteries primitive or tribal). 'Archetypal' might be better – 'archetypes' is the psychologist Jung's nickname for the preferred patterns of thinking in the human brain – a very mixed bag of matters which range from the built-in to the culturally acquired, and exist at all levels of consciousness; they certainly include all the residues from primate days which we

have been discussing, as well as much else which is both primate
and human – the infantile anxieties which spring from the
development of primate sexuality into human character, for
example. Such archetypes are, generally speaking, the current
matter of the 'dream time', of ceremonies, of legends and the
like. They are the ways of thinking which come most easily to
Man as a species. They are best thought of as grooves in the
mind down which our mental processes most easily run unless
we stop them and into which our thinking falls with a positive
'click'. Science is very largely a technique for preventing our
thinking from behaving in this way, and the ability to overcome
such ingrained and emotionally satisfying patterns and criticize
them is the main breakthrough which the scientific method
makes possible. At the same time, they are a product of primate
evolution and an inseparable part of us. We were probably
developed in a context very like that of the Australian Aborigine
in which this built-in programme was positively used. The
programme is still there in all of us, and unless we use and
satisfy it, it will break out where it is not wanted – often to the
defeat of all our plans.

This, indeed, is the reason that we must separate 'religious'
experiences of this order from religion as it appeared to our
eighteenth-century ancestor, and the fact which ordains that
we must do so lies in the human brain, which has come so far,
and achieved its most recent breakthrough, by the process
which has generated the anxieties we need to allay – by the
development, that is, of a sense of reality. In socializing Man
still further we have the uniquely difficult problem of dealing
with his 'fundamental unease', the clash between wish and
reality, unacceptable impulse and social need, without spoiling
his ability to go on distinguishing between the two. This ability
is precisely what all the major religions occupationally blur. It
was no great problem to the Aborigine, who did not confuse
the 'reality' of the Great Snake who vomited up his ancestors,
and whom he depicted in sinuous mounds or lines of feather-
ornament, with the real presence or absence of a snake in his

path, or a water-hole where the ground looked *so*, even if he did not verbalize the difference. The Hindu probably does not view the Endless Recurrence of Time in quite the light he views the seasons or the financial year. We do not confuse dream events with real events, though both have functions (some peoples do in fact confuse them). But our problem is that our growing grasp of reality, beside increasing some of our anxieties, has contaminated 'religion' with historicity, to the point at which it was necessary to break with religion in order to achieve science – including scientific insight into our unconscious life. A sense that we are part of the mind of the Universe is an emotional experience. A statement that the universe was made by someone sharing our mental processes is quite another matter. To feel deathless, within the 'dream time', is one thing – to assert it as fact, and with details, that we shall survive death as persons and go to heaven is quite another. 'Religion' of the first kind is about Man, not God, and devoted at root to human feelings and wishes, which it organizes, as does art. It celebrates the creation of moral and spiritual experiences in the course of primate evolution – illustrating some more universal features of the natural order, it is true, but chiefly important to men because made up of human feelings, and not in any other sense 'universal' or 'all-explaining'. If anything it reconciles us to reality by asserting the autonomy of an unconscious life. There are very few 'eternal verities' at the other, physical, level, and most of what there are, from our point of view, are insupportably unpleasant. 'Liberation' says the *Mahānirvāna Tantra*, 'does not come from hymn-singing, sacrifices or a hundred fasts, but by the knowledge that Man is himself God.' True, but to be really liberated we have had also to face up to the realization that God is no more than the marvellous creation of Man, and cannot 'save' us.

It is in this sense that science, which has so often and so loudly been accused of weakening our moral stamina and setting us in conflict with eternal verities, has actually proved the most uncompromising moral creation of Man. It imposes on us a moral courage in the face of reality which is difficult to maintain at all, and impossible, given our unconscious minds, to maintain always, but nonetheless an obligatory part of humanness from now on. When Darwin was faced with the obstinate assertion that Adam and Eve, profoundly important inhabitants of the 'dream time', were also historical figures like Napoleon, religion in its old sense had already been overtaken by this new realization of the importance of factual truth, without having yet acquired the new moral virtue of integrity towards that truth.

From the time that religion and historicity became confused, the ultimate outcome has been inevitable, and because the original function of religious activity, the allaying of anxiety by resolving it, remained obstinately active in the new, inappropriate setting, that outcome has been very painful for many people. Religion, instead of dealing with feelings, had come to deal with factual matters. The discharge of anxiety has come to rest more and more on belief in untrue facts, and less and less upon an emotional operation at the deeper levels of mind. We no longer exorcized the fear of death by being able to feel deathless – we had to believe as a matter of fact that we were deathless. We were not content to experience the sensation of being at one with the Universe, we had to believe in a Universe driven like a train by an anthropomorphic God who was as factually real as is an engine driver. Until the scientific confrontation this kind of issue could be blurred, but from then on it could be blurred only at the cost of going into reverse, of cultivating, not exorcizing, irrationality – of denying the real in pursuit of the wish. Science has gone round and round like a reaper and binder, reducing the area of cover in which God might be hiding, while those who claimed to preach truths which were unchanging, yesterday, today and forever, searched desperately for some means, any means, whereby the formulae of an age which believed in the real existence of devils and miracles could continue to be used in some sense, any sense, if necessary a Pickwickian sense, by a modern age.

It is the fundamental quality of science that its chief value, the acceptance of truth over wish, is self-policing. If we cultivate illusion or wish at the expense of what is, of the reality principle, our machines will not work nor our crops grow. The habit of mind which comes from that discipline cannot be fenced. Its tendency is to spread throughout our thinking. 'Religious' experience, in the sense that the Aborigine knows it, is a reassurance only, and probably an integral part of human-primate sociality. Religious *belief*, based upon such experience though it may be, is even for the martyr and the ascetic an act of self-indulgence, a willingness to settle for a lesser intellectual integrity in order to escape from the cold of insecurity, indeterminacy, and unfulfilment. Religion in its original role discharges our anxiety without denying it. Belief, by contrast, blunts our awareness of the human predicament, for that is its function, and in accepting it we become less social because less human; the predicament is one of the things – possibly the most important – that we share. The psychiatric importance of this is immense, for it is only through the integrity of science that we have been made able to admit to ourselves what we are really like, without fear and without denial, while still separating what is from what is not, and yet without the sacrifice of human emotions and drives. And as we shall see, its social and political importance may be no less.

Psychoanalysis – the discussion and experiencing of various unbiddable emotional forces in a stylized social setting, either by confrontation with a therapist or couch-style, with the therapist suppressing himself as a social presence – is really itself a 'ritual': one appropriate to our culture, because it involves a fair amount of factual explanation. Western-trained analysts who have tried it on the Yoruba (who believe, among other things, that dreams are real events) have found that witch-doctors within the cultural tradition get better results. Their rituals are appropriate to their patients' cultural heritage. In a sense, to say that a man's troubles are sent by the ghost of his grandmother, and then lay the ghost, is a rational therapy. If we say: 'Your emotional problem has its origin in the old primate business of mother-avoidance and fear of castration; it hurts more to fear one's mother, so you, by cultural consent, push the whole thing back to your grandmother: you need to get over the semi-built-in fear that she threatens your identity and potency by being female,' then this sounds more Western and factual, but the outcome, if the appropriate experience is provoked, will probably be as beneficial. In a large sense our way is 'better', because it involves a recognition that these are studiable processes, and there should be research into the correctness in real terms of the biological guesses behind them – correction by such research will give a still better therapeutic result. At the same time we are not, as people, more rational than the Yoruba, only more rationalized, and much more discursive in intellectual terms. We do not believe in ghostly grandmothers, but they can very well haunt us nevertheless.

The scientist is in an interesting quandary *vis-à-vis* depth psychology – whether he appears as a patient or attempts to comprehend his own scientific activity in more general terms. By training he attempts to base his factual judgments on the presence and weight of evidence, and to exclude emotional factors and experiences from them (though if intelligent he will recognize emotions as facts, at least to the extent that they produce effects and are a substrate for study). Intuitive thinking is the enemy which science was developed to control. Offered a psychoanalytic interpretation, one may be inclined to question it because it looks unlikely at the conscious level, or because of unconscious resistance to what it reveals, or because it appears to exemplify the type of thinking which a scientific training teaches its subjects to avoid. There is an apparent difference here between interpretations offered in general terms – in Freud's books, for example – as part of an intellectual justification of what is in effect a scientific theory, to be judged as such, and interpretations offered by an analyst to a conventional scientist in the analytic situation. In the first instance there is no reason to allow psychoanalytic ideas a special rate of exchange – like any other ideas they depend on evidence; one part of the theory to be established, however, is that the ideas themselves are uniquely able, for intelligible reasons, to disturb us and to evoke resistance, which is in turn a perfectly observable and studiable phenomenon. The scientist undergoing analysis who required an experimental demonstration of every interpretation offered to him would not, however, get very far, and the analyst who attempted one would not be a very good analyst – in getting insight into raw emotions where these are once exposed, he will need to be guided by theory and training, but his most useful implement is his own intuitive use of the emotional equipment which he shares with his patient, so that in the event the theoretically unsound therapist able to work 'off the top of his head' with a deliberate suspension of self-criticism may get better results than a more rigidly critical thinker. At this particular point in the growth of human self-comprehension the two ingredients in our current dilemma meet: we are a species capable of rational abstraction, but obliged to think (and motivated in most of our choices of subject, interest and range of vision) by irrational forces which have an intelligible pattern for us as a species – as individual scientists we are attempting rational abstraction, but are using individual brains which contain irrational emphases typical of the species but patterned by our own personal genetic and experiential history. The scientist is not unfamiliar with the idea that a principle of uncertainty is introduced when an instrument with built-in biasses is used to study itself, and this may be a good point to begin his emotional education. One could regard a right assessment of the claims of reason and unreason, hard and soft-centred thinking, and insight into their relationship as the major neglected field in scientific training today, and the psychoanalytic study of the motives, resources and limitations of science as one of the most important of barely tapped projects. Much has been written and more surmised about the psychological origins of art and the psychoanalysis of individual artists, with the implication, in the eyes of the common man, that artists are a more disturbed and irrationally motivated group than the rest of us. True, they are often more aware of their unconscious sources, and more readily allow themselves to exploit and express them, for art is largely, in our culture, a vehicle for such individual expression. Scientists – the other main group of the vocal and inspirational – are equally drawing on, driven, inspired and handicapped by, the emotional resources of Man. As a group they are commonly refugees from these resources, however, who combine propulsive curiosity with an attempt to produce a wholly reality centred end product. I have seen much argument about the effects of therapeutic analysis on artistic creation, but precious little about its effects on scientific creation. Such studies are overdue, for certainly scientists are the group in our society where the general human dilemma of reconciling the recognition of irrational needs and resources with the need to maintain rationality – the dilemma of the interrelation of thinking and feeling – is the most acute. They are also the group on whom devolves a large part of the responsibility for leading the culture in the direction of a solution, and their emotional education is a high practical priority. It is a heresy in rationalist quarters to suggest that particular emotional experiences are a prerequisite of good science, yet like other heresies it appears to be true. The importance of the priority is heavily underlined by the writings and practice of scientific psychiatrists of the veterinary persuasion, whose resistance to their own emotional background and aggression towards their patients are disturbing even to colleagues who do not quite see what is wrong with them, but recognize them as 'cases'. The late Sir Arbuthnot Lane, that brilliant surgical technician who devoted his declining years to excising normal large intestines, and urging patients to undergo the operation 'while there is yet time' to be cleansed, has his psychiatric counterparts among the brainwashers and the battery henhouse behaviourists of psychopharmacology and aversion therapy (not that these techniques have no contribution to make in the treatment of mental disease – simply that there is a correlation between the zeal of their devisers and a patterned and disturbing lack of judgment). But it looks as if therapeutic advance in psychiatry, the growth of judgment and non-alienation in science, and the move towards a more relaxed and less alienated culture may all depend on the extent to which those who have chosen the conscious realism of science become able to get insight into the part which their own unconscious motives have played in that choice.

On a banni les démons et les fées, said Voltaire; *o croyez-moi, l'erreu a son mérite!*

The art and ceremonies of 'primitive' or tribal peoples are really a complex technology designed to manage and deal with emotional needs in the frame of each particular culture. It is the most successful technology of such cultures, far more sophisticated than any equivalent in our own society – probably because it is the only technology which works well on a basis of intuitive planning: there is no deliberate design or research behind it. Conversely, since the need is intuitive, our kind of technology, which has quite different objects in mind, often finds itself serving a truncated function of this kind unawares. In the last century 'religion' meant Christianity as we know it, and 'art' the production of objects to put in galleries or on pedestals in squares. Neither of these had the emotional efficiency or concentration of a South Seas mask, even when this is treated as an object and isolated in a museum, without the ceremony which it was designed to fit. Yet time and again engineers working with no objects beyond the design of a hard-headed, functional machine did manage to produce unconsciously objects of almost equally strong primitive appeal. The nearest Victorian equivalent to a ritual mask or an ancestor figure is perhaps the steam locomotive – intended to pull trains, not to appeal to our unconscious mind. Yet for all its functional intent it managed to focus, unbidden, many of the attributes of emotional function which we see in an Easter Island figure – personality, sexuality, augustness, an alarming and at the same time a benign quality;

what in primitive art we call the 'numinous'. Locomotives, ships and bridges were the real Victorian gods, and their success is an eloquent illustration of the way in which emotional needs succeed in squeezing into wholly practical contexts when we fail to express them deliberately. In the same way, one does not need to be a psychoanalyst to recognize the emotional and unconscious associations and functions of the intercontinental ballistic missile, the war god of the present century (one might, in fact, wonder if it has any real function other than emotional ones). We begin here to encounter a less pleasing aspect of the unconscious motives behind engineering; the whole project of missile construction is in itself an irrational one. So are many human projects, in origin – it is with our 'dream time', not our purposes, that their origins lie. In the case of bridges and loco-motives, if not of the capitalist drive for wealth and production which generated them, the results, in spite of some drawbacks, were in general worthwhile for their own sakes. Whatever the 'dream-time' origin, the results stood up to some of the practical tests of reason – as the psychoanalysts would say, the super-ego approves the rationalization; we have found a reasonable use for the results of our unconscious drives. This is true of scientific ideas generally – they start in limbo, but our conscious intel-ligence prunes them into useful shape. In the case of giant rockets the process is far less complete. They would be as functional in cardboard, and less dangerous; as to doomsday machines and atomic weapons, these are war gods pure and simple – dangerous outgrowths of our unconscious fears and anxieties which technology has unfortunately made able to carry out the fantasies of destruction and hatred which they express. We would be richer and safer with the effigies of older gods of death, and we might be less dangerous to each other if we accorded them the appropriate ceremonies of appeasement.

The manifestations of science and technology are not always what they seem. If we looked for an incarnation of modernity, we might well choose the astronaut – the master of technology who depends on it to go where nobody has gone before and return safely, in the pursuit of science. But what does he do? After undergoing great preparatory austerities, in which 'his flesh is all but torn from his bones', he is finally 'called' to his supreme test. Putting on a special garment and wearing a mask fit for an other-worldly undertaking, he ascends to the top of a tower, is sealed alone in a minute capsule, and then, on a 'ladder of arrows' (an excellent name for a multistage projectile) he circles the earth and returns. One day he will reach the moon. In so doing he is enacting in remarkably close detail the characteristic exploit of a shamanic wizard or an Eskimo *angakok*. His ordeal differs from one which has been with us since the Stone Age only in its literalism. While the shaman in his flight to the moon will cross the perilous bridge, open the defended door, and find his spirit-wife, his *anima*, from whom he will bring back healing powers for his neighbours, the astronaut will find only – the moon. One may wonder if the extra expense of literalism in enacting this venerable human rite is entirely justified. Shamanic spirit-voyages at least gave us epic poetry, and their technological enactment gives us science fiction; quite possibly the most culturally beneficent consequences of space travel may be those that the astronaut himself least intends, for modern *angakut* and their social 'infrastructure' have in some senses less insight into what they do and why they are doing it than the Eskimo variety. Many of our present scientific forecasts are in fact paranoid.

The brain is an obstacle to scientific thought. It is an obstacle in the sense that it is the co-ordinating centre for human movements and appetites. It is necessary to think *in opposition* to the brain.
(Gaston Bachelard)

Fair enough, and in order to achieve the scientific revolution, we have devised a technique for doing this. On the other hand it is not possible to *live* by pure reason, 'in opposition to the brain' and the emotions, without that organ revenging itself on our health and sanity. Moreover, having acquired the scientific method, and a discursive knowledge of our own unconscious, against the grain, we now have the task of applying it to give us satisfactory and fully human life – which can only be done *with* the grain. The more naive notion – that psychology and pharmacology, once they were sufficiently advanced, would conquer and dispense with our intractable emotional needs and turn us into embodied intelligences devoid of irrational content – is moonshine, and if they did we should be neither human nor capable of further activity. The objective exercise has been necessary and well worth while, and we must never allow it to become submerged again by archetypal thinking, fantasy, or a recrudescence of the confusion between myth and objective understanding. But we are now ready to face our emotional needs armed with the power of becoming objective when this is appropriate. All that is necessary is a clear separation of modes of thought, into those appropriate for finding out facts about the external world, and those appropriate to satisfying the requirements of being happily human. This semantic no-man's-land is governed by the fact that we still use brains to think, and that thoughts and observations must go through them, does not really present great practical problems. We can avoid the fate which overtook 'soft-centred' Chinese or Indian science and philosophy, which is so acutely aware of the lack of a real frontier between ourselves and the 'outside' world that it failed to effect the abstraction necessary to make the scientific revolution possible: having made that step, we can go back to universalism and to a sense of identity with, and 'non-violence' towards nature without being hamstrung by it or getting sentimental over it.

Indeed, given intelligence, this is no more difficult than the normal practice of abstracting, for mathematical purposes, an ideal gas or an ideal soap-bubble. Neither resembles a real gas as it exists in a cylinder, or a real bubble as it is blown from soap-suds. Still less does it express our experience of them. To the critic who points this out, we can say, 'We know; but let us over-simplify for the moment, so that we can see what sums need doing. These will give us an opening into the problems which affect real bubbles and gases, and we can add the complicating factors as we go. The result will be useful to give us new human techniques and potentialities. It does not mean that we shall stop enjoying the experiences of breathing fresh air, or looking at iridescence in bubbles and letting them remind us of the pleasure we had in being breast-fed.' Indeed, under-standing does not cramp living – it widens it; but it is not a substitute for it. We need the ability to switch from one to the other, or combine both, without being worried or compulsive about the process. Our newly won power of abstraction is not a skin but a boiler-suit, which should be put on or taken off as required. We need to learn to live in our skin, like Adam, and put on our boiler-suit when we have a job in hand.

'Religion' of the primitive type is one socializing expedient which makes us aware of our human archetypal 'programme'. Art is another – in fact, in the Aborigine's context, the two are inextricably mixed up. As with religion, art in our own, post-technical society has come to mean something quite different; for a start, it has lost most of its social content. The pessimistic German philosopher Max Nordau pointed out this shift of meaning in the case of dancing. Dance is one of the most important 'primitive' social activities, a strong post-primate impulse which uses our response to rhythm, movement and so forth for social, emotional and cohesive purposes. To us it is a specialist art form or a popular recreation – when its older powers reassert themselves, and a cinema-full of teenagers begins to experience the older meaning of 'dance', we send for the police. Nordau glumly predicted that all art would go, eventually, the same way. Certainly 'our' sort of art – the art produced by individuals called artists, most of whom are militant individualists exploring the old human patterns in their own minds, and relying for the impact of their work on the hope that others will recognize and share them – is a pallid thing compared with the intensity of corporate feeling and emotion in the Aborigine's cult objects and mystical patterns and some-thing quite unknown to him. We make little conscious use of it in his sense of the word, as a source of shared human experience.

At the same time it has kept its original vigour better than religion, because it trespasses less on the fields we now recognize as belonging to reality. We still recognize and admit that art is a proper source of emotional insight, a context where we can allow ourselves to have irrational feelings unashamed. Nobody takes Vincent Van Gogh's sunflowers for a botanical diagram – we can both agree that real sunflowers are not like that, and that real sunflowers *are* like that when they have been through the human mind. The confusion between the emotional function of the Aborigine's religion, and 'religious' statements about cosmology, astronomy, or evolution, which deprives modern religions of much of their older human function, is far less evident in art, which remains one of the few contexts where we can safely let ourselves acquire insight from emotional experience without having to make reservations about reality.

A proper use of art – guided now by some of the reality-based insights we have obtained from anthropology and psychology – looks a more hopeful means of developing our emotional life and satisfying our emotional needs than a revival of the Greek mysteries or the Aborigine's dances. In it, the old primate and human impulses, both social and antisocial, both loving and hating, could very probably be satisfied, and satisfied socially, without the risks inherent in letting them swamp our thinking. If we did celebrate any Eleusinian Mysteries which were relevant to our own culture we should probably call them drama or poetry rather than 'religion'. If we could use art in this way, we might achieve the solution to our biggest problem as a social species at this stage of our development – the need to direct our affairs by terms of reality and reason, while making use of the old, built-in emotional programme of Man for the task which it evolved to fulfil, the constructive expression and discharge of a social animal's emotions.

At the moment we have no good way of doing this – the old programme is still there, however, and when it breaks through into our behaviour it is a source of active danger to us all. At the moment, our planning of the world is not directed by sociality or by reason, but by the eruption into politics of archetypal ways of thinking which are as risky to the safety of us all as a recrudescence of baboon dominance behaviour would be. Race hate, the Bomb, dogmatisms and fanaticisms of all kinds, personal illness and suicide, as well as gentler and more sociable irrationalities, are all examples of reason breaking down under the continued bombardment of impulses from the 'dream time' – and while in their original setting constructive and destructive drives of this kind have averaged out in favour of human sociality (otherwise we should not be here), under present conditions it is the aggressive impulses, and those individuals most dominated by them, which most readily break through. Jung was called a Fascist for pointing out that Fascism involved such an unwelcome breakthrough of archetypal unreason. If we intend to survive our present technical achievements we must find vehicles through which we can both express and control our emotions, instead of letting them break out into violence or fragmentation, or hamper the proper use of the world's resources as they do today. Hitler longed to be an operatic composer. It is unfortunate for millions of people that he had no talent, and was obliged to act out his emotional conflicts with real lives and live ammunition. A return of art to its original human functions might save us from further disasters and shocks of this kind. To this extent, teenagers who dance and yell ecstatically have the right idea.

The origins of the confusion between the factual element in religion and the emotionally functional lie in the nature of an important human cultural tool, the myth. To the Christian and the rationalist tradition, a myth means by definition an untrue narrative, especially one which is believed out of ignorance or superstition, in contrast (according to taste) to the historic truth of Christianity or to scientific and historical fact. To the primitive, however, a myth is something quite different. It is 'true' and at the same time holy, and it differs from purely imaginative story-telling; but the line between its 'truth' and solid matters, such as the right way to hunt, or the best way to plant rice, is blurred. In essence the myth is a tool in the emotional operation which we have been describing as the 'programmed' function of religion in human societies. It is a story dealing both with the real (the world and its origins, death, birth and techniques of living) and with supernatural figures which are considered as real in a different sense; these are inhabitants of the 'dream time', within which their deeds and words are conceived as lying. Whether the persons of the myth were ever real – like Robin Hood, King Arthur or Christ – or wholly imaginary, like Father Christmas, is not of primary importance. For the primitive, the myth differs from other stories in many important ways; it often purports to explain matters outside his range of investigation (the origin of the world, or of his own ancestral customs) and mimics the consequences of scientific knowledge in that the knowledge of the myth confers control over events; unlike a historical story, however, the myth is a continuing process, outside time, and requiring re-enactment, so that the world, the crops, or the custom which it explains may be renewed by the activity of the individual. If the Easter story commemorates a historical event – the death of a Messiah who rose again, on one specific past occasion – then Good Friday and Easter commemorate this, as we might commemorate the battle of Waterloo. If the story is a myth, in its anthropological sense, then whatever happened at the first Easter, Christ is dead again on the evening of Good Friday; his worshippers mourn him as truly dead – and on Easter day they raise him from the dead by their acclamations. Such worshippers have a sense of true participation in the event they celebrate, and believe that if they did not celebrate it, their God might remain dead. The battle is to be won again every year, by each generation.

We must put ourselves into this unfamiliar frame of mind in order to understand the interplay between factual, functional and emotional forces in prescientific religion. Myths, like orgies, arise in our own culture unbidden and often to our hurt. In order to bring our ideas of human origins within the scope of objective study, we have had to dismiss and demythologize the myth; however much emotional satisfaction it might now give us to believe that the world was created in seven days by an anthropomorphic God, and that the Garden of Eden was a geographic location, we could only do so with the sacrifice of our most important cultural weapon, the objective examination of Nature and outselves. We could not now celebrate death and resurrection without asking ourselves in what precise sense we think that a dead person may survive or rise again. The 'stories which confer power' are now scientific stories – if we know the real origin of smallpox we can control smallpox. Yet this removal of an important emotional tool has left a gap in our equipment, which we recognize when we experience the difficulty of devising psychiatrically practical release rituals, or when we detect ourselves yearning for some 'secret' the possession of which will confer on us the emotional benefits which primitives derive from initiation.

Odd vestiges of the old human 'programme' crop up in all kinds of unexpected places. When surgeons dress in white, put on masks and gloves, and 'scrub up' for operation, their routine has a definite function – to avoid infecting the patient or themselves: yet no anthropologist attending an operation can miss the deep emotional satisfaction which such a 'ritual' or mystery confers – if it did not, we should long since have devised simpler and less dramatic types of asepsis. If we are challenged, we shall say that all this is not strictly necessary, but it helps to impress the need for cleanliness on probationers and students; in other words, we are 'initiating' them. In scientific culture, such self-appearing rituals are concerned with relatively trivial matters so far as emotional adjustment is concerned. Our only true pursuit of origins which confers insight and imparts knowedge is the time-consuming individual pursuit through depth psychology which takes us beyond myth by dissecting the 'dream time' itself.

· · · · ·

The Eleusinian initiates, says Aristotle, 'suffered' or 'experienced' rather than learned.

'Insight', in the psychiatrist's sense, is not information so much as feeling (lectures explaining a man's complexes are not the equivalent of working them out emotionally with an analyst) and the 'insight' acquired from this emancipatory process is not knowledge, nor is it definable in terms of true or false, which is why admixture between this type of religious experience and the dogmatic religions, the interpretation of fact about the universe, and other true/false propositions is undesirable. What such experiences can produce, if misused in this way, is an unjustified sense of conviction which is proof against reasonable argument. On the other hand, taken simply as devices to generate states of feeling, they could prove extremely useful. We do not underrate the beneficial effects of listening to a symphony because it imparts *this* kind of insight without imparting information. They interest us now because it looks as if the human brain is programmed to benefit from the 'oceanic' sensation which these various devices, suggestive and physiological, produce. No doubt the sensation itself is a cerebral trick, a final common path which can be set off by various means, but we may have kept it precisely because primitive Man found it socially and mentally advantageous. If we are programmed to experience this type of release, we make little use of it now, except when it appears unbidden in mental disorder or in response to drugs, hot-gospelling or 'beat' music. Yet it might be a most useful tool in our biggest current task, that of keeping a clear head in conscious and socially purposive contexts, free of compulsions from the 'dream time', without bottling up our irrational drives and suppressing the dynamism which they generate – and on which our rational behaviour depends for its energy.

Chapter 9

The Human Future -
A Technology of the Emotions

WHAT then, is the answer, and what, if any, are the social and mental forces which can make humans fully social, give them the power of joy without limiting their capacity for necessary sorrow, and enable them to be free of anxiety without blinking the facts of the human situation? Philosophy, religion, religious and stoical resignation have all been prescribed. Oddly enough – or perhaps not so oddly – the psychiatric evidence seems now, in many people's view, to point to the same force which socialized primates, made us able to live in families, and motivated our personal and social behaviour, namely sexual love – extended, through the peculiar role it has come to play in human economy, far outside its original context of the desire to copulate, and made more similar to the poet Schiller's idea of 'joy'; a sexual affection, carrying the same pleasureable intensity we find in man-woman relations, but spilling over into all types of relationship, even our relationship with things. Some may feel that psychiatrists and poets are both enthusiasts who have sex on the brain, and may wish to cry 'Steady!' at this point. Primatologists, however, cannot be justly subject to these suspicions – and it is from the primatologists that this concept of 'eros' (love transmuted into love-of-living and love-for-your-neighbour) now draws much of its support.

It is symptomatic that we think of the irrational, or rather the unconscious, part of ourselves as an enemy – a fund of ill-controlled drives liable to eventuate in such unpleasant and dangerous manifestations as war, suicide and self-destruction generally, or, at a less spectacular level, to frustrate our attempts to live by applied science. It can indeed be this, but it is also our most important human stock-in-trade, because in it most of our behaviour, and especially those parts of our behaviour involving imagination or creativity and strong motivation, also arise. The analogy to atomic (or any other) energy is very close. Art, we have long known, originates in our irrational half – but then for many of us art is a dangerously anarchic activity, and artists borderline mental patients whose art, as well as their traditionally irregular behaviour, threatens our respectability. But the human unconscious is also the driving-force behind our rational science. Science has long been depicted as a process of wholly conscious thought, which fuses our practical wishes, our reasonable cogitation, and the innate curiosity which is one of our more respectable irrational drives, invited into the parlour because it is useful. True enough – in its final stages it is and does. But people become scientists and study particular topics with engagement for reasons as deeply rooted in their childhood and their unconscious as any work of art, and the imaginative process which leads to original thinking about scientific matters is as Dionysian as any other 'creative' inspiration. The scientist has to be reality-centred thereafter, in order to work out his inspirational hunch and see if it really squares with the external world; but his ability or compulsion to settle particular questions, as well as his ability or inability to see particular facts, depend wholly at root on the same irrational mechanisms as other human creativity, insights and blind spots.

The interplay of these forces is the most fascinating and important thing in our age. Science has been developed over the years to enable us, by adhering to a reality-centred technique, to domesticate some of our unconscious drives and resources. It gives its practitioners not only useful results but profound emotional satisfactions. It has opened the possibility of pulling ourselves up by our bootstraps, because it has been turned round and reapplied to our own minds – that we recognize the unconscious and study it, albeit hesitantly, through such methods as psychoanalysis, is a product of science. Directed at first only to the control of this side of ourselves by reason, so that it does not balk our understanding of things or appear unbidden as a source of dangerous behaviour and illness, the study of the unconscious is now approaching the point when we can reapply it once more, not simply to avoid neuroses, but to increase our creativity and sociality. Now we are beginning to understand, we can afford to stop being afraid – or only being afraid. We have spent the last three centuries attempting to tighten our intellectual and conscious grip on ourselves. This we still need to do, but we are getting to the point where further progress will depend, not on relaxing that grip and going back to gods, myths and our infantile residues, but on becoming able to relax intellectually and enjoy the basic irrational satisfactions of living, loving, imagining and even hating, for which we are biologically and mentally programmed. Art and 'release' generally are little holidays of this kind (Paul Klee's name for them) and we are beginning to need a holiday. For once we have the prospect of being multi-level human beings who can both feel and understand without letting the two processes interfere with one another. In doing this we have resources potentially greater than those of the Greeks.

The study of depth psychology certainly does not tend towards any fatuous optimism about human behaviour; it actually alters the balance very little compared with a reasonably sober prescientific view – that human beings are capable of great good and great evil. The balance has shifted a little, however, in the way that this particular truism is interpreted. Our eighteenth-century ancestor would have been quite clear in his mind that the violent, destructive and self-destructive half of Man represented his 'animal' or atavistic side, and the social and moral counterpart his characteristically 'human' contribution. Without any cynicism, there is some ground now for reversing the attribution, or at least expanding it. Self-destructive trends are rather rare in animals, except where functionally built-in; major intra-specific aggression and predation are rarer, and become rarest in social species and in the higher primates – no animal fights as Man does, and the general pitch of potential and actual self-destructive behaviour which he reaches is quite unique in phylogeny. It is, in fact, one of his most characteristically 'human' features. On the other hand rudimentary sociality and mutual aid are relatively common in lower animals, both as programmed instinctual activities, and apparently, in close correlation with intelligent behaviour. Our capacity for love and sociality, as well as our more-advertized 'moral sense', are in direct continuity with this part of our animal inheritance. A large slice of our capacity for aggression is associated with, or expressed as, alienation from this 'vegetative' and animal mode. Aggression and self-destruction tend to take over, in Man, some aspects of sociality and altruism, reversing their sense, and talking volubly about self-denial. This is in full accord with Freud's picture of the nature of civilization, but love and physical satisfaction, the life of unselfconscious sensory experience which is the baby's frustrated aim, and possibly (if we do not read it too much in the light of human attitudes) the animal's achievement, is what we are, in intellectualized societies, alienated from: we have been taught, by the time we reach adulthood, to distrust it – the mystic and the drug addict pay short and expensive visits to it by more or less artificial means; art and religion, of the functional as opposed to the factualized and dogmatic kind, are raids on it; work, play and in particular sex, can bring us close to it, but all such glimpses lack integration. Without any anthropological romanticism it often looks as if some simpler cultures, though less prosperous, manage this better – though by no means all, and unless one had lived in them it would be rash to enthuse about their advantages. But the paradox still remains, that while our culture traditionally views the life of the senses as 'lower' and antipathetic to the strenuous discomfort required by virtue, the facts all point the other way – to a correlation between the senses and our more benevolent and social face, and between repression and denial of the senses and our more murderous side.

An eighteenth-century optimist would have seen Man as a social animal liable to outbursts of irrational aggression; he now looks to us more like an irrationally aggressive animal capable of outbursts of sociality. This is his typical appearance in large, civilized societies – subcivilized and small societies may be invoked to support either definition. Now civilization has been very largely the process of devising technologies. Is the task of dealing with our murderous and promoting our agreeable side a technology? If it involves taking intelligent thought to achieve an object by the use of appropriate means, one answer to this is 'yes'. But it is not a technology with quite the ordinary rules which have applied to the abolition of disease or the making of steel; first of all, it involves feelings as its field of activity, and the interaction of feelings and of intellect in projects of this kind is complicated by the fact that the technologists themselves have unconscious minds, irrational needs, and the like (so they have in rocket-building or even a constructive venture such as surgery, but when the feelings and needs themselves are the substrate, the conflict becomes unusually acute). Secondly – or rather, as a rider to firstly – the objective technique which is needed for a technology is itself an alienation from unconscious needs and from simple feelings – we need to 'think against our brain' in order to get things straight. Primitives have developed, in their art and ceremony, what look like emotional technologies, without this problem, because they have, as it were, poured them straight from the pot, by a process of intuitive growth which did not sit down to plan its moves, nor say, 'Come then, and let us deal wisely with them.' Our kind of technology would have to take thought – in psychiatry it already attempts to do so – with the double risk, on one side of turning into the kind of veterinary brainwashing which some 'realists' favour, but which exudes as much aggression towards the subjects of its ministrations as did the Inquisition, and on the other into a kindly process of intellectual exploration which often works, but lacks intellectual stamina *vis-à-vis* the genetic, physical or political causes of human unease, and abhors objective demonstration. It is only the old problem over again, that to survive in comfort, or to survive at all, we have now to learn a new synthesis of thought and feeling – to think without alienation, and to feel without surrendering conscious reason. This is in the direct primate tradition. Our evolution has been the interlocked evolution of intelligence and emotional behaviour. Its next stage has to be purposively managed by us.

Freud's idea of infantile hedonism is distinctly naive so far as animals, and probably also Man, are concerned. The 'drive' behind animal behaviour appears to be less a pursuit of physical appetites, as a plus quantity, than an impulse to minimize tension – and certainly not the cultivation of appetites in order to enjoy satisfying them. Animal displacement activity, and much human behaviour, normal and abnormal, is essentially tension-reducing or tension-avoiding, even though, in the case of Man, such behaviour which is fixed in infancy may excite new and intractable tensions later on. There are exceptions – play-behaviour in dolphins and otters, for example, looks like *joie de vivre* for its own sake, though one could probably devise a function for it. Sexuality in Man – which is the appetite which Freud really had in mind – could have acquired the same autonomy with the acquisition in higher primates of the power and the social need to mate continuously instead of intermittently. In some cultures, as Devereux says,[10] it is a displacement activity; this is largely true of our own. But in general it looks as if the non-alienation which we (perhaps wrongly) attribute to 'simple' cultures is not so much pleasure-seeking, and due to uninhibited libidinal energy, as tension-free. The pleasure of such a state, reflected in the Golden Age myth, is something we have many of us experienced as just falling within the range of childhood memory: it is not so much a discrete physical pleasure as a pleasure in being, which we recognize chiefly by contrast with later anxiety or unease. It is this, rather than the cultural equivalent of the 'furious fornication' of Japanese prints, which the erotization of life really implies; it is non-compulsive for a start. Rites of liberation, even if they make use of pleasure activities such as sexual licence or intoxication, have the same final end, so that a religious 'orgy', however wild in its machinery, is a tension-reducing, not a kick-producing device; kick-hunting is a late and unsatisfying manifestation of personal and cultural unease. Something similar is embodied in normal sexuality as opposed to its compulsive versions, for the satisfaction of complete orgasm lies as much in the state of non-tension which follows it as in the preceding sensory excitement.

One could easily fuse, or confuse, these two views by taking pleasure to mean 'that which is sought', *appetitum quid* – which would square Freud's libido with animal and human observation, but the difference in shade of meaning is worth drawing, especially in a kick-hunting culture; our fetishistic assessment of pleasure has its mirror image in Freud's moralism. A non-alienated society would be quietly self-enjoying rather than frenetic on the lines of *Brave New World* – though to achieve this state it might well use means of abreaction more extreme than we now find acceptable. The difference is one of aim.

For a long time we have taken for granted the view which Freud derived from his reading of Darwin, that primate social evolution has proceeded by repression: in order to achieve society, we have 'given up' unrestrained instinctual gratification to the disciplines of work, monogamy and the like. Without this repression we should spend our time fighting like so many devils for mates and castrating one another out of spite. But in fact this is something which no known primate does – possibly the nearest approach to the diabolical horde which obsessed nineteenth-century biology is the dominance of baboons, but this is a state not more diabolical than the inequalities of Man; certainly not Dante's Inferno, which we are led to believe would result from non-repression. We see far nearer approaches to this unenviable state in the consequences to society when repressed aggressions break out, as they did at Auschwitz or Hiroshima, or in those who contemplate the murder and suicide of the entire human race. We sense in Freud's view – based, certainly, on the best biological opinions of his day – yet another mirror, not of primate potentialities, but of our own anxieties.

A biologist might now put this very differently. So far from 'giving up' the primacy of sensory – especially sexual – satisfactions, higher primates develop them in non-sexual contexts and thus sexualize (and socialize) their whole behaviour; however, in the formation of human societies such drives have come under the control of custom, the energy for that control being generated, like our fear of the murderous horde we should become if left alone, by our own infantile anxieties. It has been argued – often by the transparently anxious, but nevertheless with some substance – that 'civilization' is the fruit of repressing our wishes, especially our sexual wishes, and our love of pleasure, in the interests of stamina. True or false, this looks itself like the residue of an infantile idea, that repression brings its own reward. The reward in question may well be the busy energy which has given us our science, wealth and technology, plus gastric ulcers and nervous breakdowns. If that 'reward' has also included Auschwitz, and much less-spectacular suffering and unfulfilment, one might perhaps still argue that the exercise was unavoidable and retrospectively worthwhile in sum. What such repression has never, apparently, yielded is spontaneous sociality, for this depends not so much on frustrating erotic drives as on transforming them to become not merely genital but universal; as, indeed, prehuman primates transmuted sex into sociality and the type of all affectionate social relationships, the family. Evolution did this for them – we have to do it for ourselves. One might say that in the Garden of Eden all relationships with persons and things were thus 'libidinized' – taking advantage of the human ability to sexualize everything, even work and pain – but in Eden nobody had yet said, 'In the sweat of thy brow shalt thou eat bread...'

Eden is not a historic state but a human potentiality, and there are societies which have come close to realizing it, giving to all their activities the undifferentiated libidinal zest we see in young children. This is a primate ability in contrast to the dominance-society of baboon days: oddly enough it is the industrial, acquisitive revolution, which saw our own society at its most baboon-like, which has put us in reach of realizing the Edenic and un-baboon-like potentialities of our other socio-sexual selves by removing the compulsion to hard, compulsory and acquisitive work. 'Free' societies are ebullient or gentle, but not 'hardworking' in the competitive sense.

We may well be on the verge, or on the verge at one remove, of an era in which *this* kind of work – drudgery – is done away by automation, and eventually (if we can keep our own psycho-pathology in check) of one where frenzied acquisition becomes even more irrelevant than it is now, because there is no shortage. We have a distinctly sticky patch to cover before that can occur, however, during the years when the demands of those who still plough with bullocks and die of starvation will require to be met, whether or not that means less gracious living in the countries now privileged. Yet ultimately, and perhaps soon, we can expect the world to be free both of drudgery and of compulsive acquisition, unless we preserve them deliberately for irrational ends. In one sense we are here and now enacting a myth – the most august of them, that of a 'golden age' – but with the reservations prescribed by a sense of reality.

The problems of a society over-endowed with leisure are not as far removed as this – we have them already in embryo. At the same time, 'leisure' as boredom is not a characteristic of wild primates, nor is too much of it tolerable for us as a species. 'Work', said the anarchist Proudhon, 'is the first attribute, the essential characteristic of Man.' In other words, we need to be doing something in order to be happy, and work which is not crushing nor compulsive is a socializing force equal to art and religion, which can discharge both aggression and constructive drives in one act: lack of this sort of work, involving physical activity, is one of the probable origins of the odd and growing outbreaks of malicious damage through which some people in urban societies seem to vent their energies against objects. We have tended, since the end of pioneering days, to equate work with acquisition and independence, whereas in most small-size cultures it is as social an activity as art – whether it is communal agriculture or our own particular 'mystery' or craft which gives us status.

So far the Marxist half of the world has paid more lip-service to this use of work than we have done. But the point is a valid one, and the growth of leisure, if we are not all to get on one another's nerves, must eventually mean the growth of leisure *in which to do the work we wish*. Professors know there is usually something wrong with an idle student – either he wants to do something other than the course in hand, or, if he really wants to do *nothing*, he is sick. In animals work merges with play. Play is one of the most interesting of all forms of animal behaviour, covering as it does such games as are a form of training, corporate chasing and running games, and mere ebullience like that of the dolphins or the otter. As such it is most evident in social and semi-social animals, and most evident of all in Man. Play, which joins hands with art on one hand, through make-believe, and with love on the other (since play with a sexual partner and with children are two of the most psychologically important kinds) is another human-primate socializing force in which we can express and discharge emotion without prejudice to serious purposes.

These types of human behaviour (religion in its original 'archetypal' sense, art, work, sexuality and play) are probably the materials for the further emotional and social evolution of Man – they have been effective materials in his past evolution. To direct them we have now the assistance of growing rational insight into the way in which these forces operate and have operated, in past societies and in our own. Had our eighteenth-century ancestor discussed human nature, he would probably have expressed himself as an optimist, who thought it was basically good, or a pessimist who believed in original sin and thought it was basically bad. We differ radically from him, in that we know it is both, and cannot say it is either – only that it is highly complex.

It is difficult, of course, not to be over-anxious about the possibilities. This is as critical a point for our evolution as the appearance of tools or Oedipal jealousies, and since things are moving now at the accelerated speed of social, not the slower speed of biological, evolution (a) we have much less time to waste and (b) we must take action ourselves, not leave it to selection, which acts in a different time scale. At the moment our intellectual development and technical abilities as a species have outstripped our means of social and emotional expression, and the situation is bound to be precarious until the balance is redressed. That it can be redressed, by the operation of the stabilizing factors I have outlined, seems clear from both psychiatry and anthropology – we can enlist science to deal with this problem as it has dealt with epidemic disease. Meanwhile, however, there are intractable matters such as the inequality between fed and unfed, the growing capacity of governments to tamper with the human environment, as well as the older idiocies, dominance-patterns and rivalries of baboon days – which draw added force from our unconscious needs, and now, in terms of budgetary expenditure, occupy most of our physical resources, as pyramid-building occupied those of the Pharaohs.

The aim of effecting a rapid change in human behaviour is known as revolution, and we should have a theory of it. What theory we adopt will depend upon our preconceptions. Revolution considered as once-for-all, rather than a continuing obligation, is only the myth of Eden over again. I wish here – since this is a biology book – to put forward one consideration only concerning successful revolution, a consideration stemming from what we have said concerning 'breakthrough' behaviour in primate development which is the model of past successful revolutions in human capacity. The difficulty facing every revolutionary is to know where to start. If we could suddenly alter people we could alter society. If we could suddenly alter society we could alter people, once they got used to it. Missionaries and anarchists have tried the first, revolutionary parties the second. One can imagine the 'evolutionary demon', whom we sometimes use as a convenient abstraction in discussing biological evolution, pondering that if he could get apes to use tools they would have to stand upright, and if he could get them to stand upright they could begin to use tools.

Or let us imagine a discussion concerning revolution in any real university (a real university being one where no opinion is barred and no revolutionary afraid to speak up). We are considering not only 'human nature' but how to feed twice as many people by the end of the century. This, says a Marxist, is an economic matter – unless we alter the system of work, profit and production, how can we succeed? Yet 'profit' is not a built-in human drive, says the anthropologist – if we alter our whole culture-pattern via child upbringing, we shall alter our attitude towards wealth and sharing without the necessity of shooting any *rentiers*. The origins of the block to doing this, says the psychoanalyst, are not rational but unconscious – bring everyone to a measure of insight through analysis or otherwise, and the job is done. So how, says the Marxist, do you set up a programme on this scale so long as vested interests oppose it and it has to be made to pay before we begin? And so on.

There are two non-biological comments to be made on this. One is that all three are undoubtedly right in some particular – economic, cultural and individual psychic life in societies must and do both change in step and change each other. The other is that for any urgent task it is reasonable to tackle first the one which looks easiest. This, however, is not trouble-free: Lenin altered Russia's economic life, but the state he founded is only just overcoming the cultural legacy of its past and the psycho-pathology of some of its leaders – one could find similar warnings nearer home.

If the analogy of past evolution has a bearing on society, however – and here it has far more than in the past, when

'Darwinian' ideas were rashly invoked to prove political theories – it suggests that breakthroughs occur by the edgewise advance of three, four or more attributes of an organism, or a society, to the point at which there is an effective breakthrough of one of them – from which point, instead of the processes of change being self-conflicting, they become self-reinforcing. If I could detail the changes here, and the order in which we should attempt to promote them, the breakthrough would no longer be a matter for evolution, it would have occurred already. Perhaps this has indeed happened. The basic conflict which holds us back today is that between technical skill and unresolved psycho-pathology. Two centuries ago, a fanatic or a rationalist, a tyrant or a democrat, could make equally good guns, even though they might not be able to train equally enthusiastic soldiers. That is no longer quite true – psycho-pathology in office, while it can still express itself in bombs, poison and the like is less and less able to express itself in new and fundamentally original science. Hitler did not get the bomb because he could not tolerate free enquiry. In a sense the Sputnik reflected the end of Stalinism. One must hope that this is so. Certainly in the biological sciences and the social skills on which the new revolution must depend, only the unrigid and the liberal-minded have much chance of making fundamental discoveries. Once further technology, as well as survival, comes to demand social and emotional advance as a prerequisite, we may have got over the hump.

One very significant indication that baboonery is at long last on its way out will come when we cease to regard government as a matter of power and begin to regard it as a matter of communication. The two have been badly confused throughout human history. Political power is not, phylogenetically, a direct descendant of baboonery: though there has always been dominance behaviour in human societies, the food-gathering period was probably non-authorian (societies of this sort still are) and institutional power *may* have been a historical correlate of settlement and property (this was a favourite arguing point of nineteenth-century libertarian socialists). Baboonery soon came in, however, and since the development of institutional authority, human societies have used 'government' to express two incompatible social activities, namely organization or communication and individual or group dominance behaviour – whether of the eldest, the strongest, the entrenched or the magic-possessor, who is the ancestor of the technologist. We all know what dominance behaviour is – in some human societies of a crudely competitive sort it really was baboon-like. Baboonery carries with it a rudimentary equalitarianism, however, in that as in the old West if one *could* be strongest or quickest on the draw one could make one's own status without questions asked, and there are in every troop baboons who rise by brain rather than by brute force. Human and primate dominance are also linked to the family and the dominant position of the father; this is important because, as a species, we tend easily to use society as an extended family, and accept a father-substitute who orders us about, with complacency if not relief. Commoner than true baboonery or paternalism has been the vesting of dominance in an institutional group of possessors – possessors of things, of knowledge, or of respected pretensions. This has had some social function in the past as a stabilizer of social patterns. But in all cases crude dominance-behaviour has always been ready to take over, in that beside accepting and discharging the useful functions of government, such entrenched people or groups have also very often used their position to claim the satisfactions which big baboons get by force (food, sex, leisure, the deference of others), or very much worse, to use the opportunities accorded to them, not for such understandable if reprehensible class advantage, but for a far more dangerous form of play therapy – the use of power to discharge their personal conflicts and abnormalities, and even, as Hitler did, to incorporate them into society. The difference between the two types of abuse is evident enough – we now disapprove the first (we do not expect people in office to admit that their position gives them food, women, wealth and free travel; though they get all these, they must pretend that they put up with such privileges in the public interest only) but we should do better being governed by the corrupt and sensual, who at least value their own skin, than by fanatics bent on suicide – who are often exemplarily austere and abstinent; in other words, who hate themselves as much as they hate their supposed enemies.

I do not want here to go into the biology of class struggle in the past or present, though classes and *élites*, like 'races', do have some, albeit minor, biological implications apart from social behaviour. My point here is that power institutionalized in society has split exactly as our own behaviour and emotions are individually split, between reasonable even if selfish purposes and irrational, self-destructive or aggressive drives. This is not surprising, since power is exercised by people. Our ancestors would put up with the tantrums of a King Henry VIII and even regard them as kingly, or fatherly *à la* gorilla silverback, in exchange for the social, political and emotional functions a strong king discharged. But with the greater stability which came through increased centralization and civilization we have come both to resist such gorilla-parental airs as anti-human (though parliamentary governments will adopt them as freely as King Henry if they are allowed to get away with it) and to see that we have been led, through the old infusion of dominance into organization, to take the wrong point. Our eighteenth-century Man would certainly assume that Man requires someone else to 'make' him social, though he would be having qualms about who should watch the watchers. Modern Man still thinks the same, but only if he is not a psychologist, anthropologist, or social scientist generally. This is a big and important split in our thinking; Western social biology has now an entirely different outlook on human behaviour, and particularly on the control of antisocial human behaviour, from that of institutionalists in our own culture and of other cultures such as that of the Communist world. One sees this split most obviously if one compares the attitude to crime and its prevention or treatment between those who work in scientific human disciplines and those who do not. Partly this is a split between two kinds of personality – those who are by nature empirics and liberals (who take up social science for personality reasons) and inbuilt 'tough guys'. But it still does not invalidate the point that the old prop of authoritarian government – that because Man is naturally savage we need to be tough to keep ourselves under – is scientifically behind the times on evidential ground, and that what best reintegrates our most troublesome citizens is the concern, not the hatred, of their fellows.

We have a long and an uphill road in incorporating this knowledge (for it is, now, knowledge and not opinion) into our society in Britain and America – let alone in all the other urban societies of the world – against the vested personality and power interests of those who prefer the other view. It may be longer and more uphill than the incorporation of Darwinian ideas or Freudian insights has been (it attacks all the sacred cows, economic, social and irrational) and yet such a view is already making headway. It was only just over a century ago that we stopped hanging children – we have now stopped hanging anyone. There are and will be laggards, but this is a trend which goes beyond mere civilized repression of the violence in us – it has scientific ground, though in itself it may give rise to problems by permitting us one less form of hatred. There is a real sense in which the criminal, public or private, is a human sacrifice whom we can openly hate and torment to save ourselves from still more ulcers.

This is yet one more branch, then, of the problem of 'libidinizing' our relations (or, in plain, getting rid of hate and self-denial in favour of spontaneity). A society with little bottled-up aggression would have to conscript itself a government for lack of volunteers, or alternatively do what I said a while back and recognize that the useful half of government, aside from its function as a vehicle for our personal or public death instincts, is a problem not on coercion but in communication.

A traffic light is a communication device. The reason it is

needed is not that drivers are so aggressive that without it they would deliberately drive at each other (though some would – the aggressive use of motor vehicles is a problem in social psychiatry I cannot really exhaust here) but rather as an external arbiter of who should go first at an intersection. This is needed because drivers have no time to say 'after you'. One could use a policeman. But (to pursue the analogy I was making) policemen can get too big for their boots, baboonwise, or be corrupt, or make plain mistakes. A machine has no faults of character and no unconscious or conscious axes to grind. It makes government into pure communication. We might do a lot worse in the future than be governed by machines, provided we keep our own character faults out of the programming.

The mechanics of democratic expression are a straight problem in communication theory: with modern techniques it would be quite feasible to have not only an informed public opinion, but a continuous, objective measure of majority and minority wishes – a democracy as direct as that of the old Greek city or the small club, with everyone consulted on every issue (the links of this with what we have said about intelligence, about greater leisure, and about many other matters I leave to your discussion); how this feedback influenced the community's action would depend on how the community or its computer was programmed. The chief practical snag, with societies as they are, would be to prevent rigging of the market or the programme. At the moment a similar system is used by politicians to stay in office – they take opinion polls to find out what we want, then mould their propaganda to fit our wishes, and may, if compelled, even mould their programme. A machine is a reality-centred thing, with no ambitions unless we build them in, and no unconscious mind unless we give it one, on purpose or inadvertently. We might find it safer to put a machine at this point in the feedback loop than to let people stay there. In fact, whether we do so or not, it would not at the simplest be necessary for 'democracy' that everyone be consulted when every decision is taken, any more than we need use our will-power to approve the digestion of our dinner – action, as it is today in democratic politics, would still be largely negative where the voter was concerned. We require not a range of alternatives we could dial, but simply a red button labelled NO, placed too high to be reached without getting a chair. We would press it when we were dissatisfied enough about the *general* conduct of affairs to bother to get the chair. The machine or the administrators would set out to act according to their lights, and we would keep them in line. This arrangement would only mechanize what we now have in a more complicated and less reliable form.

It is difficult to find any common denominator between human 'ecstatic' techniques, save that they are effective, dissociative and often endowed with sexual overtones; the 'reward' represents a final common path – the techniques include, beside drugs and physiological intoxicants, a wide range of stimuli or sensory deprivations. Some, like dancing or noise, are frank excitants; others have an intrauterine look about them, such as rhythmic drumming or lying bound for hours in a dark igloo (is drumming most effective, one wonders, when its frequency lies in the usual range of the maternal pulse rate?) Psychiatrists have done little by way of experiment with these do-it-yourself methods, leaving them, in our culture, to their more motivated patients, but have shown great interest in the 'utopiate' drugs, which are more controllable and less dependent on effort. The older methods are rediscovered regularly by individuals seeking kicks or by whole industries – until the advent of television in the home we all sat regularly in darkened igloos to witness psychosymbolic enactments produced artificially on a screen rather than in our own exalted imaginations. Art, pop and non-pop, is a distributive technique for such ecstatic, carthartic or entertaining experiences – our rather frivolous and awe-less approach to it suggests the wholesale distribution of a powerful medicine by naive islanders who have discovered that it tastes pleasant. It has none of the fierce integration which we see in the primitive uses of spectacle. Many primitive dissociative techniques are susceptible to discussion in terms of psycho-symbolism, as fetishes or as substitutive rituals. But this does not dispose of the biological possibility that they are still 'programmed' – that evolution has made use of our psycho-sexual peculiarities for social purposes, and has even developed them. If we saw them in birds we should say they were a part of the natural history of the species. It was a blind spot of Victorian rationalism – which recognized that Man was a primate – that it did not develop a similarly unevaluative approach to anthropology until after Freud had defined neurotic and normal behaviour in equally evaluative terms for our own culture. Some of this moralism we probably need to unlearn (ecstatic techniques and social ceremonies, however fetishistic, masochistic or otherwise kinky their content, at least appear to differ from the private version in leading to a large and lasting measure of 'release', which deviant substitutes for 'normal' sexual and personal relations usually do not).

'Erotization' of experience looks biologically quite hard-headed. We may indeed be programmed for it – our program-ming certainly evolved in primate and early human settings very unlike the social environment of today. We have seen how often and how assiduously human beings try to produce 'oceanic' feelings of well-being by means extending from dancing and heroin to yoga, sex and meditation on the Passion. I suspect that these sexually tinged and euphoric sensations – described as peace, knowledge, completeness, oneness with God and the like, which mystics both primitive and sophisticated induce with much hard work as fleeting and occasional aurae represent the operation of some of these unused 'punch-cards' – cerebral mechanisms evolved at earlier stages on the way up; I further suspect that their original function is social and tranquillizing, and that some of our psychological problems, as well, no doubt, as some of our intellectual achievements, arise from their non-use – from having at some stage in evolution 'switched them off' as spontaneous and continual experiences. If they are another derivate of sexuality (as not only Freud but the practising and highly intelligent mystic Ouspensky thought they were) that would be well in line with the primate expansion of reproductive behaviour into social living. Without going overboard for the enlightening effects of meditation or drug addiction, it might still be interesting to look into their nature and uses of 'oceanic' feelings in cultures which still find a place for them. They have interesting consequences for our ideas of mental normality, too. In a discursive society, schizoid tendencies make a misfit: in one which expects its spiritual exemplars to dissociate, they make a shaman. This is no stranger than the fact that in a non-literate culture wordblindness would be an undetected disability, but it is relevant to what we have said about the diversity of normals. Non-sexual ecstatic states are rarely spontaneous in modern England, except among schizoid or epileptic subjects, but the history of religion shows that it does not take much suggestion to set them off epidemically, at least in their crudest, abreactive or Beatle-like form. We can say, with proper intellectual sobriety, that there is something here and it might possibly be useful.

We are in any event more various than we have liked to admit. Psychiatry would have the support of biology if it suggested that we are programmed to display schizoid, fetishistic, ecstatic, bisexual and other presently inconvenient responses, to think archetypally and to believe in magic because these potentialities in some or all of us have in the past been socially adaptive. Evidently there is no place for a moralism of normality where human behaviour is concerned.

Until one sees it in its primate context, the idea of erotizing the world looks like eyewash, or, to a hardboiled Freudian, regression to the boundless self-centredness of infancy. But primate evolution is a respectably scientific discipline – it gives the more armoured among psychiatric rationalists intellectual permission to distinguish between regression, which is certainly self-centred, and non-alienation, which ought not to be (whether the patient or subject will be able to achieve the distinction will depend on his own capacities and the skill of his therapist if any – which is the main objection to amateur Zen and excursions into reefer-smoking by basically disturbed people). And many solid psychiatric citizens now verbalize the 'task' of pairing our capacity for knowledge with a capacity for feeling in this way. Thus Marcuse[11] writes about substituting the 'order of sensuousness' based on aesthetics for the 'order of reason', the idea being not to go native but to 'harmonize the feelings and affections with the ideas of reason, (and) "deprive the laws of reason of their moral compulsion...reconcile them with the interest of the senses".' The inset quotation is from Schiller. Heady stuff, perhaps, but one begins to see its social relevance when Marcuse goes on to argue that the necessity to work is a neurotic symptom and a crutch which we need only to assert our own value to ourselves, if it occurs in a society where work by us is not necessary. Heady stuff again, and not a pretext for decadent bourgeois slacking in a society where others have to work for us. We can accept it now when we see idle people having to create useless activities to keep their self-respect – knitting socks for missionaries or collecting old newspapers for the Liberal party. But this kind of non-activity may spread as automation spreads. Already we see technology being used to create employment. One could argue that fifty per cent of the 'work' done in a modern capitalist society like that of the United States by ad-men, politicians, sociologists, gun-makers and even solid scientists and psychiatrists is play-therapy, non-work, so far as the non-neurotic needs of humanity are concerned. The same probably applies to much of the organizational – as opposed to the manual – work done in socialist countries; it exists to enhance the self-esteem of the doers, not to benefit anyone else. It is against this compulsion that the beatnik is an exemplary protester – he may be regressive and escapist, and it would not do if we were all beatniks or contemplative monks or plain bone idle, but it is good that a protest against non-work should be registered by someone.

As to the other dangerous thought, 'polymorphous eroticism', so scandalous to the Puritan (who invented non-work so as to leave no time for his feelings to catch up with him) it is neither sexual high jinks nor a return to the foetal attitude, but a recognition that spontaneity cannot be prevented. 'Psychotherapy and liberation are completed in the moment when shame and guilt collapse, when the organism is no longer compelled to defend itself for being an organism, and when the individual is ready to own his unconscious behaviour.'[12] It can and should co-exist with rational intellect (there is a morass waiting in such formulations for the sentimentalist) and ought in fact to assist it, by cutting down the interference of our repressed emotions with reasonable projects, and by killing together the two dichotomies, body/mind and reason/feeling, which we have been obliged to erect in the course of development to our present cultural state. And as we have said before, this sort of insight requires to be experienced, not explained. We today may be uniquely ready, compared with the ancient Taoist, the Christian mystic, the Eleusinian initiate, or the aboriginals our ancestors, to accept it without wallowing in it, precisely because we have come to accept the moral requirement to understand and criticize; now we can proceed to develop the moral requirement to feel and to accept.

We do not yet know what makes for the choice of science in its most talented exponents. Scientists, it is said, often come from rather puritanical families and pick their future interest at a very early age – one is tempted here to look for a fusion of sexual curiosity, which is the engine, and a resolute choice of objectivity as against feeling, which is the armour, of the future fighting vehicle. To support such a guess one has at present only introspection and the superficial inspection of colleagues, however.

The mastery of social and unconscious drives, the provision of a technology of the emotions, the more productive understanding of 'inspiration' in art and science, the use of intuition as an intellectually serviceable tool, and the forming of a new, non-discursive concept of 'knowing' which includes us in our observed environment are quite possibly all connected. They seem to involve a step in intellectual method as radical as was the invention of the scientific method. That involved the acquisition of the 'language' (in computer terms, that is) which made it possible to use effectively the logical powers of our thinking-equipment: this involves a similar operation, to get the key to its analog and pattern resources. The two are not mutually exclusive, but supplementary – we already use them serially, albeit rather clumsily, when we get 'inspirations' or 'hunches' from our analog mechanism and then operate on them logically to produce science. Users of such inspirational material, both artists and scientists, never cease to be impressed by the virtuosity of this uncontrollable analog side of ourselves – its speed of operation, its fertility of invention; if we could use it reliably, instead of depending on random bursts of activity, we should be geniuses to a man – indeed, a genius is someone whose analog mechanism is unusually active, and allied to the intelligence and the emotional drive to make use of what it supplies.

In trying to explain what poetry 'is about', Mr Charles Davy[13] prints a fascinating account of a boy chess-player who was encouraged to free-associate about his game. From fantasies about the pieces he came to perceive the whole game, not serially, as vector moves, but in depth, as a Gestalt. If the king was surreptitiously removed, he did not notice that a piece was gone, but found the pattern now 'meaningless'. Finally he became scared that he would not be able to 'get back' to the normal pattern of sequential thought. This is not unlike the analog facilities unveiled by some deliriant drugs, or by religious exercises of the insight-giving type. The schizophrenic suffers from being unable to turn them off. Possibly the answer to a great many of the problems I have been describing, which interest poets, scientists, psychoanalysts, epistemologists, communications-theory men and anthropologists alike, lies in acquiring the analog 'language' of the human brain to supplement its logical language, the scientific method. There are large outlines here which I cannot fill in, but the idea makes sense. It is largely the analog language which the artists, the psychotherapist and the primitive medicine-man already employ, without really being able to handle it purposively. Scientific method was designed to limit feedback from this side of ourselves into logical operations, but it uses only one-half of the resources of our computer, the other half throwing up the hunches and motivations, but needing to be excluded from observer-type thought processes. If we can use it, however, while conserving scientific and logical objectivity as and when they are appropriate, we will have learned to use the whole computer in the setting 'for' which it evolved – one which includes ourselves within our environment, rather than as fictional bystanders.

In the light of our new-found morality of truth, unitary solutions of all human problems deserve our suspicion. I have been offering one in the manner of the non-religions, which is to solve not only our personal problems but our intellectual difficulties and our bifurcations of knowledge between thought and feeling – with the hope, since our social aims and our behaviour would both be changed by it, of milleniarist anarchism thrown in. Suspicion would be abundantly justified, at least equal to the suspicion our great grandfather ought (we see retrospectively) to have entertained for the perfectibility of Man by Reason. And yet if he failed to let suspicion undermine his enthusiasm he may still have been right in an oversimplified way, for what cheered him was the idea that Man and 'human nature' were purposively modifiable. Such ideal forecasts are objectives only – we shall not realise them 'in one', any more than we shall become wholly healthy or free, or know everything and run out of further material for study. They will engender in execution their own unforeseen snags, which will make us look optimists to our grandchildren and compel them to undertake further re-education in directions we cannot now foresee. All that this means is that human evolution has been transferred from the chromosomal to the cultural level. We ought to be able to harbour purposes without illusions.

We ought also to be on the look-out for the wilder optimists – the psychiatric equivalent of those of our grandparents who thought that railways would make us good, free and equal without further complication – and for the soft-centred, who, in the first flush of non-alienation, ascend into the stratosphere where all human relations will have their dragons' teeth extracted by Insight and even death itself will be exorcized by the realization that the ego is an illusion and our real goal is Nirvana. Against this kind of facility commonsense and bloody-mindedness, two of our most valued evolutionary cultural achievements in Britain, rightly rebel – not at the level which attacked railways because they obviously would not work and would poison the atmosphere, and space travel because it was obviously insane, but at the more balanced level that the Universe is large and basically unsupportive of individual aspirations, and that if our ego is not real, it feels real and gives us satisfaction. Such rebellion against root and branch neo-Buddhists is not illusion so much as healthy feedback – learning to deal with the intolerable does not consist in the psychiatric or the religious pretence that it is not there, for this involves the suppression of equally valid human needs and feelings in favour of pollyanna.

Important consequences follow from what we have said about the non-coercive view when we discuss revolution, as we did last in evolutionary terms; this view makes the evolutionary pattern yet more important as a social model. We are debarred by our own terms of reference, if change is to be a truly evolutionary process, from offering precise solutions of the normal manifesto type, because worthwhile revolutionary activity, like education, the rehabilitation of criminals, or psychiatry is inherently non-directive – it aims to create conditions in which people can direct themselves, and in which changes are not imposed to our specification, but grow to fit our polytypic and polymorphic fellows. Propaganda for change becomes an enlargement to society-size of the psychiatrist's problem – how to give insight, remove irrational fear, release energy, and enable the patient to decide for himself. This is a new approach, especially for the expert who 'knows' the answers, and implies that to the discipline of integrity required by science we shall have to add a discipline of humility; this should come pretty naturally from our subject, if we are learning much from it ourselves.

Some have seen the logical end (if it has an 'end') of the process of human evolution in still more ambitious terms – a takeover bid, no less, for the Universe making it conform to human moral aspirations – creating a God, as it were, to our own specification and putting him in the saddle. The fore-shadowers of such an outcome are, perhaps pardonably, vague about means and timing: others are content with the idea that Mind will somehow be rendered universal by human efforts. Evolution through Man is tending, they suggest to a

harmonized collectivity of consciousness, equivalent to a kind of superconsciousness. The Earth is covering itself not merely with millions of thinking units, but with a single continuum of thought, and finally forming a functionally single Unit of Thought of planetary dimensions. The plurality of individual thoughts combine...in a single act of unanimous Thought.... In the dimension of Thought, like the dimension of Time and Space, can the Universe reach con-summation in anything but the Measureless? (Teilhard de Chardin)

There are no prizes for an answer to the last question, which is fully airborne in its own right. True, one can see vaguely – (Teilhard sees everything vaguely) – what he is getting at. In a sense we are already establishing the Primacy of Mind, though we have a long way to go in making its communication–system foolproof to the point of unanimity-in-diversity. We might also detect processes in the universe at large which make it possible to ascribe mind-like properties to evolution, and which would neither assume that it was organized by a benign old gentleman, nor that it is an extension of our own minds; it would be edifying to recognize them, but not necessarily more so than the recogni-tion we already have of, for example, the analogies of stepwise progress in pre- and posthuman evolution. The most likely process to be common to evolution, the operation of the human mind, and the operation of minds in society is perhaps that each will prove to be a system in which a process of selection acts on a process of random variation to produce an apparently 'purposive' or directional progress. Such a recognition would give us a sense of intellectual identity with the processes which operate outside us, but not much else. It would not prove that 'God is a mathematician' addicted to the Theory of Games, though it might prove that each of these three orders of process is a little like a computer. We are not very likely to be able to take over the Universe for Mind without limit – and indeed it is not love of Mind which is the cause that agitates us in the face of the stars in their courses but a sense of personal imper-manence and impermanence as a race, both of them justified by every realistic consideration, and both highly unpleasant. When it comes to the crunch, we personally will die, and Man will eventually die out. It is to unpleasantnesses like these that religion of the factual type (by denying the facts) philosophy (by suggesting that we should not feel they matter) and intel-lectual demagogy of the Teilhard variety (by making an inspiring noise) have all tried to apply a salve. None have quite succeeded, partly because they fail in integrity, but also because they lack pity. It is no answer to the dislike I feel for the idea of dying that my genes will persist to produce higher achievements, or that my thoughts will join a kind of moral Van Allen Belt around the human race. My dislike of the idea remains as deep-seated as that of any Australopithecine – and had an Australo-pithecine seen a vision of his posterity possessing the world he would still have disliked not being there to join in. Death, our own and others, means separation, and we are social animals for whom 'parting is all we know of heaven and all we need of hell'. This is, like so many of our deepest feelings, an irration-ality from the standpoint of Pure Mind – but it is also part of the predicament which makes us human and which gives us, among other things, the sense of pity which is part of our sociality and our moral achievement as a race. There are times when we ought to weep – and there are times when a frank admission of loneliness or fear is more 'human' than any amount of inspiring pollyanna.

References

1. Sahlins, M. D. *Sci. Amer.* Sept. 1960

2. Carpenter, C. R. *Compar. psychol. Monogr.* **16**, no. 5, 1940

3. Washburn, S. L. *Sci. Amer.* Sept. 1960

4. Hebb, D. O. and Thompson, W. R. (1954). ch. 15, *Handbook of social psychology*, Cambridge, Mass. Addison-Wesley

5. Washburn, S. L. *Sci. Amer.* Sept. 1960

6. Money and Hampson (1955). *Psychomatic medicine*, **17**, 1–15

7. Zacharias and Wurtman (1964). *Science*, **144**, 1154–5

8. Haldane, J. B. S. (1949). *Genetics, palaeontology and evolution*, Princeton Univ. Press

9. Guthrie, W. K. C. (1950). *The Greeks and their gods*, London, Methuen

10. Devereux, G. (1955). *A study of abortion in primitive societies*, New York, Julian Press

11. Marcuse, H. (1955). *Eros and civilization*, Boston, Beacon

12. Watts, A. W. (1961). *Psychotherapy East and West*, New York, Pantheon Books

13. Davy, C. (1965). *Words in the mind*, London, Chatto

Index

Index

Index